How to Navigate
Today

How to NAVIGATE Today

by

M. R. Hart

Fifth Edition

Cornell Maritime Press, Inc.

Cambridge, Maryland - 1970

Standard Book Number: 87033-035-7

Library of Congress Catalog Card Number: 68-23169

Manufactured in the United States of America

Foreword

The method of navigation described in this book is the standard one used by the United States Navy.

The method of presentation is intentionally unorthodox because I believe that it is more simple and logical to approach the subject of navigation with a preliminary discussion of the principles involved rather than to follow the time-honored method of beginning with astronomical details. Such details as are necessary will be more easily remembered when the student has a general scheme into which to fit them, rather than having to build up a final picture out of a mosaic of isolated facts.

Also, while I have tried to give a clear picture of the necessary geometrical relations, I have avoided astronomy as much as possible. The *U. S. Nautical Almanac,* in giving S. H. A. and G. H. A. directly, entirely disposes of the former Right Ascension which immediately removes the most confusing part of the study of navigation. Therefore the discussion of Time, except in relation to Meridian Altitude, has been reduced to a minimum.

The greater ease and accuracy of navigating by the stars has been stressed and navigation by the sun has been put in its proper place as a special case of stellar navigation.

This book makes no pretense of being an exhaustive scientific study of navigation. It is not intended to discipline the mind nor train the character. It does claim to give the essentials necessary for intelligent navigation.

M. R. H.

Table of Contents

Introduction

Several years ago I owned a small French car. It was, in its way, a good car and pleasant to drive after one had become acquainted with its peculiarities, the chief of which was that the batteries were so weak that the horn wouldn't blow unless the motor was racing and the headlights turned off. Rounding a sharp corner at night with two hands on the wheel, another on the horn, and another on the light switch, throwing out the clutch with one foot and stepping on the accelerator with the other, was a feat which gave me a thrill of pride whenever I succeeded in accomplishing it.

Driving that car was something that not everybody could do, and later when I drove an American car I found it a little disappointing. There was nothing to do but press the horn button, so all my carefully acquired skill was out of date and no one looked at me admiringly when the horn sounded. It was much simpler that way, but there was no public applause.

Navigators nowadays are in a peculiarly fortunate position. Their labors have been so simplified by the publishing of various books and tables which do most of the work for them, that they are more or less in the button-pressing stage. But people in general still believe that navigation is an abstruse science, somewhat in the state of development of my French horn, and that its practitioners are worthy of deep respect. So the navigator has it both ways: he presses the button, the horn sounds, and he gets the admiring glances.

The United States Naval Observatory and Hydrographic Office are largely responsible for this happy state of affairs which makes it possible for any schoolboy who can keep his wits about him to solve in a few minutes problems that used to cause strong men hours of mental anguish. The results of the government researches are contained in a few thin books which, between them, solve all the complicated formulas of navigation and leave little to do but look up the answers.

Since this is the case it is no longer necessary for the navigator to go through any detailed study of astronomy and spherical trigonometry in order to navigate his ship any more than one must be a mechanical engineer to drive a car. But just as the car owner sometimes finds it useful to know what is going on when he pushes this lever or steps on that pedal, so even the most rule-of-thumb navigator should have a general idea of what he is about when he opens his *Nautical Almanac* at page 116 and looks in column 3. A knowledge of the general principles which he is applying may one day save him (and his ship), from the disastrous effects of carelessly looking in column 4.

So instead of starting right in with the practical work of finding the position of a ship at sea, I shall give a short explanation of the theory of stellar navigation.

M. R. H.

How to Navigate Today

Chapter I

§1. Cross Bearings and Position Circles

I want to make it clear that in this first discussion of theory when I say things like, "and then we do so-and-so," those words are not to be taken too literally. All they mean is that we *could* do so-and-so, but frequently in actual practice we take a short cut. So, simply read through the first two chapters and follow the argument but do not try to memorize any details of operation.

We will begin with a statement of the problem: How do you find the position of your ship when you are at sea and out of sight of land?

The first thing to think about is: What do you need to know to find the position of your ship anyhow?

Let's say, to start off with, that you are at sea at night with a compass and a range finder. Suppose you see a lighthouse that you recognize by its flashes. You take its compass bearing*and find that it is N W. You look through your range finder and see that the light is 4 miles away. So you pick out the lighthouse on your chart and draw a line running S E from the light. You know that you are on this line somewhere because from any point on the line the light bears N W. You also know that you are 4 miles from the light, so you measure off 4 miles to scale along the line and mark off your position. (See Diagram 1.)

*(See page 71.)

So you need both a bearing and a distance from *one* known point to fix your position.

Next let us suppose that a range finder is not available, and you have only a compass. You can't fix your position now from

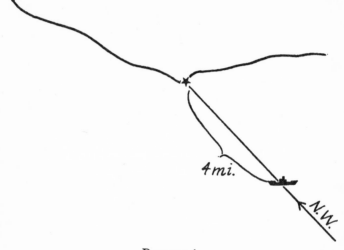

4 mi.

N.W.

DIAGRAM 1.

only one light because a bearing tells you only a direction. But suppose you can see two lighthouses. You take a bearing of each. Light A bears N W and Light B bears N. You draw a line running S E from A and another line running S from B. You must be on both lines at once, and the only place where you can be on both at once is at their intersection. (See Diagram 2.)

So the intersection of *two* lines of bearing fixes the position of your ship. This is called the method of cross bearings.

Now, finally, suppose that your compass is broken but that you have your range finder. Again you need at least two lights because a range finder tells you only distance and not direction. You find that A is 4 miles away and B is 6 miles away. So you draw a circle on your chart with A as center and a radius of 4 miles. Your ship must be *somewhere* on this circle because *every*

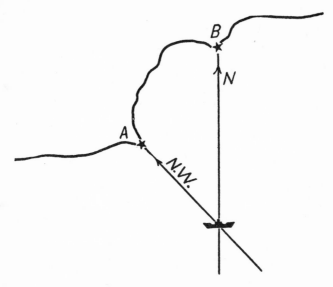

DIAGRAM 2.

point 4 miles from A is on it. You draw another circle with its center at B and a radius of 6 miles. Your ship must be on this circle too. And the only place where it can be on both circles at once is at their intersection. (See Diagram 3.)

So, if you can find your *distance* from each of *two* known points you can fix your position. This is called the method by position circles, and is the basic method used in stellar navigation.

(The astute reader has doubtless observed that the circles in-

tersect in two places, but this fact does not cause any confusion
in actual navigation as the intersections are never less than several hundred miles apart, and you select the one nearest your
dead reckoning position as *the* intersection.)

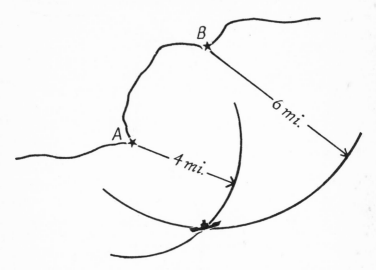

DIAGRAM 3.

So now we see what we have to do. We must get two points
whose position (latitude and longitude) we either know or can
find out. And we must have some way of measuring how far we
are from each of these points. Then we can draw the position
circles and know that our ship is at the point of intersection.

§2. WHAT IS THE KNOWN POINT K?

First of all, what do we use for our known points when we are
at sea with nothing around us but waves? Well, of course, you

know that we navigate by the stars. But we don't measure our distances directly from the stars because they are so far away that even if we could get the exact distance it would be incon-

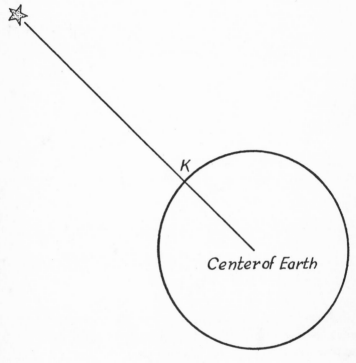

DIAGRAM 4.

venient to have to draw a circle with a radius of light-years. So we use what is called the star's projection on the earth, which is point K in the diagram. You can see that K is the point where a line drawn from the center of the star to the center of the earth, would touch the earth's surface. (Refer to Diagram 4.)

K is on the surface of the earth, therefore it has a latitude and a longitude. It isn't a fixed point in the sense of being stationary;

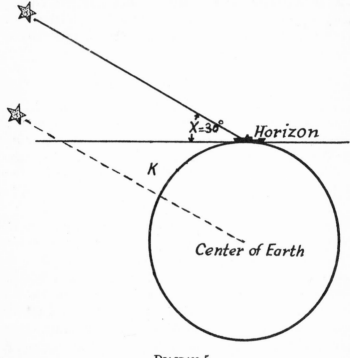

DIAGRAM 5.

it changes from second to second as the earth revolves on its axis and moves around the sun. But it is fixed in the sense of being determinable. That is to say, the latitude and longitude of the K of all the stars* useful in navigation are found from the *Nautical*

* The word "star," as used here, includes the sun, moon, and planets, as well as the fixed stars.

Almanac for each year. So we can turn to the current *Almanac* and determine the position of a star, or point K, *at any second* throughout the year. And that is all we want to know.

Now since we know where K is, if we can measure our distance from K we can draw a position circle with K as center and the distance from K as radius. The next step then, is to see how we measure the distance from the ship to K.

§3. DISTANCE FROM SHIP TO K

This is done as follows: We look at our star through the sextant, which is an instrument for measuring angles, and measure the angle X of the star above the horizon. The angle is measured in degrees and minutes and is called the ALTITUDE of the star. We also note the exact time at which we take the observation, and then find from the *Nautical Almanac* the position of K *for that star at that moment.* (See Diagram 5.)

A simple demonstration, which will be given later (see §9), shows that we find the distance from our ship to K by subtracting the Altitude, expressed as *minutes* of arc, from 5400'. The remainder is the distance from the ship to K expressed in miles.*

Since there are 60 minutes in a degree and the Altitude is 30 degrees, the Altitude is 30 × 60 = 1800 minutes. And the distance from the ship to K is 5400 − 1800 = 3600 miles. If the Altitude is 22° 30' it is likewise 1350' and the distance from the ship to K is 5400 − 1350 = 4050 miles. The greater the Altitude the smaller the distance, which means that if the star is high overhead you are close to K, and if the star is directly overhead, at an altitude of 90°, the ship is at K.

As soon as we know our distance from K we obtain the latitude and longitude of K from the *Nautical Almanac* and then, with K as the center and the distance as radius, we can go ahead and draw one of our position circles.

Nautical mile: The U. S. Coast and Geodetic Survey mile of 6080.20 feet and the Admiralty knot of 6080 feet have been adopted in America and Britain as practically the equivalent of 1/21600 of a great circle, or an arc of 1' thereon, the minute or *m.* in any latitude.

Then we go through the whole process again with another star, finding its altitude and K, and drawing another circle. The intersection of the circles marks the position of our ship.

So the problem of finding the position of a ship at sea is solved, at least in theory.

§4. Some Difficulties with Maps

But if you took out your charts and started to draw a circle with a 4050-mile radius you would run into trouble immediately. Ordinary navigation charts constructed on the Mercator projection are representations of a round surface on a flat piece of paper. They are therefore more or less distorted and the greater the area they represent the greater the distortion. They represent small areas satisfactorily but when it comes to drawing a circle with a radius of thousands of miles, such as our position circles, the distortion would be too great. A circle drawn on a chart with a compass wouldn't be a circle at all if it were transferred to the surface of the earth. And it would be far too much trouble to figure out the lopsided circles that we would need for our intersections. We could draw out true circles on a globe but it would have to be such an enormous globe for accurate work that no ship could carry it.

Here would be a very real difficulty if it were not for the fact that we are not interested in drawing the complete circles, but only the small arcs necessary to find the point of intersection. And these can be drawn by using a rather roundabout method.

The explanation of this method is not hard to follow but you must keep clearly in mind that all you are doing is avoiding the mechanical difficulty of plotting the position circles. No new facts of life about the stars or K or altitudes are involved. We simply want to find out how to use the facts we have learned.

§5. The Position Circle Becomes a Position Line

Let us say that we have taken the Altitude of a star, that we have found out the Latitude and Longitude of K for that star, and that we have measured with the sextant the distance of the

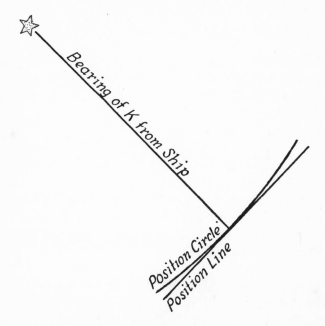

DIAGRAM 6.

ship from K. Now we want to draw out on the chart the small part of the Position Circle which contains the ship's position.

We assume also that the dead reckoning has been kept up so that we know the region in which this small section of the position circle will lie.

To begin with it will simplify matters if we observe that the small arc of our position circle is practically a straight line. The radius of the circle (which is the distance from the ship to K) is so great that an arc 20 or 30 miles long is near enough to a straight line for the difference to be neglected. And we can say that the ship is on this straight line just as well as we can say that it is on the arc of the position circle. We call this line the POSITION LINE.

The next thing to note is that the Position Line is at RIGHT ANGLES to the radius of the circle. This radius points toward K (the center of the circle), so if we can determine the bearing of K from the ship we also can determine the direction of the Position Line, which is at right angles to the bearing. (See Diagram 6.)

Just keep these facts in mind for a moment. The Position Line is a straight line *at right angles to the bearing of K from the ship*. So if, by any device, we can obtain this bearing and locate *any* point on the Position Line, we can immediately draw a line through that point at right angles to the bearing and know that our ship is *somewhere* on that line.

§6. THE ASSUMED POINT A

What we do is this. We prick off on the chart a suitable point, within 45 miles of our dead reckoning position, and call it the Assumed Point A. (§11 explains what makes a point "suitable.") We know (from the chart) the latitude and longitude of A, and we also know the latitude and longitude of K (from the *Nautical Almanac*).

Then we turn to the navigation tables (see §18) and find both the bearing and the distance from A to K.

We then lay off on the chart the line of bearing through point A toward K. Then we draw another line through A at right angles to the bearing and this is the position line of A. In other words, if our ship were at A, the line we have just drawn would be its position line. (See Diagram 7.)

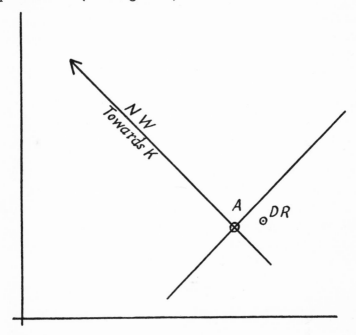

DIAGRAM 7.

This is the first step.

To get the actual position line of our ship, we continue as follows:

K is always several hundred or thousand miles from A, and A is within 45 miles of the ship. Therefore *the bearing of K from A is, for all practical purposes, the same as the bearing of K from the ship*. The position line of the ship (which is at right angles to the bearing) must then be parallel to the position line already drawn through A.

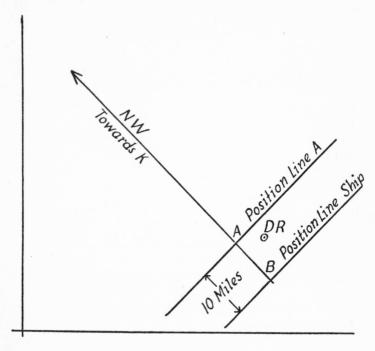

DIAGRAM 8.

Let us now compare the distance of A from K with the distance of the ship from K.

The distance A-K we have just found in our tables, and our sextant observation has told us the distance ship-K. So by simple subtraction we find whether the ship is nearer to K than A is, or vice versa, and by how many miles.

Let us assume that the distance A-K, which is called the CALCULATED DISTANCE, is 2500 miles, and that the distance ship-K is 2510 miles. Then the ship is 10 miles farther from K

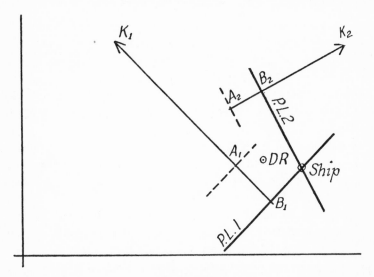

DIAGRAM 9.

than A is, and it is on a position line parallel to the position line we have just drawn through A.

Therefore we measure off 10 miles to scale on the line of bearing AK, AWAY from K. We prick off this point and draw through it a line parallel to the position line of A.

This is the position line of our ship. (See Diagram 8.)

Since it is only a Position *Line* and not a position, we must go through the whole process again with another star, another Altitude and K, another A, another Calculated and Observed Distance, and so on, until we get a second Position Line.

And the intersection of the two position lines is the POSITION of the ship. (See Diagram 9.)

§7. SUMMARY TO DATE

Let us now summarize briefly what we have done so far.

To find the position of our ship we need two intersecting position circles. To get these circles we select two points whose positions we can find and whose distances from the ship we can measure. Then with the Known Points as centers and the distances as radii we draw the circles and find the point of intersection.

We choose for each of our two Known Points what I have called the K of a star. K is the point at which a line from a star to the center of the earth cuts the earth's surface. K is not a fixed point but we can find its latitude and longitude at any given moment from the tables in the *Nautical Almanac*. We can measure the distance from the ship to K with a sextant.

Now we have all the information we need to draw a position circle. But owing to the great distances involved it is not practicable to draw the circles in full so we confine ourselves to drawing the small arc of each circle near the point of intersection. And each of these arcs is, to all intents and purposes, a straight line at right angles to the bearing of K from the ship. This line is called a *Position Line*.

In order to find where to draw the Position Line on our ordinary navigation charts we resort to the following plan. We *choose* a point on our chart within 45 miles of our dead reckoning position. We call this point, A, the Assumed Position. It is close enough to our True Position so that we can say that the bearing of K from the True and from the Assumed Position is identical.

This being the case, a Position Line through Assumed Position A, is parallel to the Position Line of the ship.

Since we know the latitude and longitude of both K and A we can figure out the *distance* of K from A, and also the *bearing* of K from A.

We draw through A a line at right angles to the bearing of K from A, which is the Position Line of A, and therefore parallel to the Position Line of the ship.

Now we compare the *distance of A* from K (which we have found from our tables) with the *distance of the ship* from K (which we have found from our sextant observation of altitude). We note the difference in mileage and also if the ship is *nearer* or *farther* from K than A is.

We lay off this *difference*, which is called the INTERCEPT, from A in the proper direction along the bearing of K, and mark point B. And through B we draw a line parallel to the Position Line of A. This line through B is the *Position Line* of our ship.

We then repeat the entire process with another star, another Assumed Position, etc., and draw another Position Line. And the intersection of these two lines marks the POSITION of our ship. (See Diagram 9.)

§8. ACTUAL STEPS

Before going on to any more theory we shall go briefly through the actual steps taken in getting and working out a position.

The first thing to do when you are actually doing it, is to get the altitudes of two stars and note the time of each observation. To do this go on deck at morning or evening twilight when both stars and horizon are visible. You pick out two stars which you can identify (if you do not know the stars by sight there are charts and tables that will help you) and take the altitude of one of them. Then you look at your chronometer and write down the time (hour, minute, and second) at which you took the sight. Then you read your sextant and write down the altitude in degrees and minutes. A minute of altitude corresponds to a mile in distance and you do not ordinarily need to know your position more closely than that.

You do the same thing for the second star.

Now you get out your navigation chart and mark off on it your dead reckoning position. After this you choose the nearest suitable point and mark it A. The method of choosing this point will be explained later (§11). A must not be more than 45 miles from the dead reckoning position.

Then you find from the *Nautical Almanac* the latitude and longitude of K for your first star for the moment at which you took the altitude, and you take the latitude and longitude of A from your chart.

Next you turn to your book of *Navigation Tables* and determine the *bearing* of K from A, and also the *distance* of K from A. The latter is called the Calculated Distance.

Your sextant observation has given you the distance of K from *the ship*. This is called the Observed Distance, and should not differ from the Calculated Distance by many miles.

You subtract the smaller from the greater distance and write down the *difference* in miles TOWARD or AWAY, according to whether the ship is *nearer* or *farther* from K than A is. This difference is called the INTERCEPT.

After this you lay off the line of bearing from A toward K and mark off on it the *difference* (Intercept) in miles. If the observed distance is *less* than the Calculated Distance, lay off the Intercept

TOWARD K. If the observed distance is *more* than the calculated distance lay off the Intercept AWAY from K.

You mark this point B. Then through B you draw a line at right angles to the bearing of K. This is your first Position Line.

Now you return to your second star. You choose a new A for it and go through the whole process again, ending up with another Position Line which cuts the first at the Position of the ship.

This process sounds complicated written out as it is here, but all it really amounts to for each position line is: one sextant reading, one chronometer reading, looking up a few figures in your books, and drawing a line through a point. After you get used to the various steps you should be able to do the whole job and get your position in less than half an hour.

Chapter II

§9. Distance from Ship to K, Sextant Altitude

In the last chapter I said that I would explain later how the sextant angle measures the distance of the ship from K, and also how we choose A, the Assumed Position.

We shall take the sextant angle first because it comes first in finding a position. We shall start by finding out why the distance from K is equal to 5400′ minus the altitude (expressed in minutes of arc). Then we shall see what corrections have to be made in the sextant reading to get the TRUE ALTITUDE of the star above the horizon.

When we take the altitude of the star with the sextant, the angle that we measure is the angle X in Diagram 10, which is the angle star-ship-horizon. But since the star is enormously far away in comparison with the earth's diameter, there is no difference between the angle X and the angle Y, which is star-O-C. So we can say, for the moment, that the sextant reading gives us the angle star-O-C, which is the same as the angle K-O-C.

Now if we know the angle K-O-C we can figure the distance K-C because 1 minute of angle corresponds to 1 mile on the surface of the earth. So the number of minutes in the angle K-O-C is the same as the number of miles in the distance K-C.

Let us say that the angle K-O-C, which is the same as the

altitude of the star, is 50° 17'. This is 50 × 60 + 17' or 3017'. So the distance from K to C is 3017 miles.

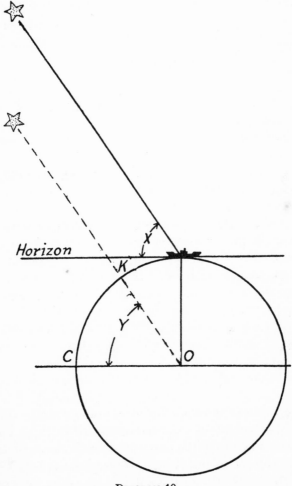

DIAGRAM 10.

But what we want is the distance from the *ship* to K. This is the distance from the ship to C minus the distance K-C. We know that the angle ship-O-C is a right angle or 90 degrees, and 90 degrees is 5400 minutes. So the distance from the ship to K equals 5400 minus 3017, which is 2383 miles.

§10. SEXTANT CORRECTIONS

Certain corrections have to be made to the sextant reading in order to get the True Altitude of the star, and now is perhaps the best time to tell what they are.

If we could stand at the center of the earth with a perfect sextant and there were no air around the earth to cause refraction, and the star were an ideal point, then the sextant would measure the exact angle star-O-C, which is what we need for finding our position.

But since our sextant may be imperfect, and we are several feet above the earth's surface when we take our altitude, and there is a lot of air between us and the star, and the star (especially if it happens to be the sun) may have a considerable diameter, we see that we cannot just take our sextant reading as it comes and call it the angle star-O-C.

I am not going to discuss sextant errors here, because the only one that will bother you, if you have a good instrument to start with and don't knock it around, is what is called Index Error.

This error can be measured by setting the sextant at 0′ and looking at the horizon. If the horizon is an unbroken line there is no index error. If the horizon is broken you must adjust the sextant until the horizon appears unbroken and then take a reading R. If the reading is to the left of the 0 mark the number of minutes shown must be subtracted from the sextant reading when taking altitudes. If the reading is to the right of the 0 mark you must add R minutes to the star's altitude. See (Diagram 11.)

To the corrected Sextant Altitude we apply another number of minutes (found in the *Nautical Almanac*) depending on the height of our eye above sea level when we took the altitude.

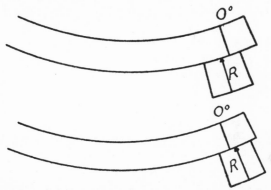

DIAGRAM 11. A (above): INDEX ERROR −R′. SUBTRACT R′ FROM ALL SEXTANT ALTITUDES. B (below): INDEX ERROR +R′. ADD R′ TO ALL SEXTANT ALTITUDES.
"IF YOU'RE ON, YOU'RE OFF, AND IF YOU'RE OFF, YOU'RE ON."

And a third correction lumps together refraction, parallax, diameter of star, and anything else there may be. It varies according to the Sextant Altitude. One of our tables tells us its value for different altitudes, and whether it is to be added to or subtracted from the Sextant Altitude. After these steps have been taken the result is the True Altitude (also frequently called the Observed Altitude).

True Altitude = Sextant reading ± index error ± correction for height above sea level ± correction for refraction, etc.

The True Distance from the ship to K is equal to 5400′ minus the True Altitude.

§11. What Is a "Suitable" Point?

Now we must see what makes a point "suitable" for our Assumed Position A, then we can really get down to business.

I said that if we knew the latitude and longitude of any two points on the earth's surface we could figure out the distance between them and also the bearing of one from the other.

You can see from Diagram 12 that from K up to the North Pole down to A and over to K again forms a triangle. The distance of K from the North Pole is 90° − the latitude of K. In the northern hemisphere the distance of A from the North Pole would be 90° − the latitude of A. The angle H A is equal to the difference in the longitude of A and of K.

So, in our triangle K-Pole-A we know two sides and the angle between them, and by using the formulas of spherical trigonometry we could figure out the length of the third side A-K, and also the bearing of K from A. This bearing is the angle Pole-A-K*.

But we don't need to bother with the formulas of trigonometry because the distance AK, and the bearing have already been determined and put in books of tables for a great many different positions of A and K. And we want to choose a position for A so that we can look up the answers in the tables and not have to do any trigonometry ourselves.

So, in our choice of latitude for A, we are limited by two considerations: it must be within 45 miles of the dead reckoning position and must appear in the tables. H.O. 214 lists every full degree from the equator to 90 degrees, so all that we need to do is to take the full degree nearest to the dead

*The line through the Pole and A is a meridian, and therefore always runs N-S. The angle Pole A-K is thus the azimuth of K from A.

reckoning latitude and call it the latitude of A. Therefore if our dead reckoning latitude is 35° 21′ N we take 35° N for the latitude of A. If the dead reckoning is 34° 48′ N we choose 35 N for the latitude of A, and so on.

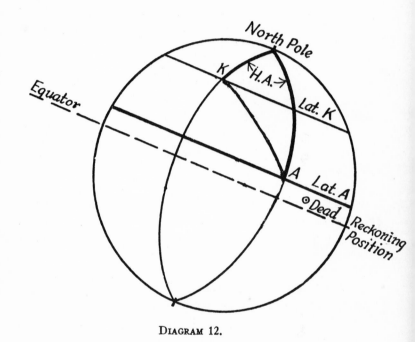

DIAGRAM 12.

The *difference* of longitudes, which is the angle H A in Diagram 12, is also listed only for full degrees, so we must choose a longitude for A which differs by full degrees from the longitude of K, as found from the *Nautical Almanac*. We choose the nearest longitude to the dead reckoning which *differs* from the longitude of K by full degrees.

If the longitude of K is 97° 42′ W and the dead reckoning

longitude is 14° 21' W we choose for A the longitude of 14° 42' W because this will make our difference in longitudes exactly 83 degrees and we can find it in our tables.

Our "suitable" point A is therefore Lat. 35° N, Long. 14° 42' W.

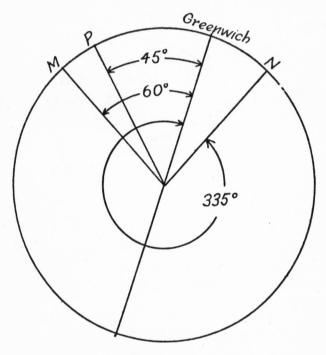

DIAGRAM 13.

Longitude of K is, by convention, always given as long. *West* of Greenwich, so difference of longitudes is obtained by *subtraction* when the ship's long. is likewise West. If the ship's long. is East, then in order to have the difference in full degrees, we must choose our "suitable" point by *adding* the two longitudes. In the above example, if the ship had been at Long. 14° 21′ East, our suitable point would have been the nearest point to 14° 21′ which, added to 97° 42′ would make a whole degree. This would be 14° 18′ E and the hour angle would be 112°.

§12. SOME TECHNICAL TERMS

I shall now have to bring in some technical terms. Up to the present I have managed to avoid them but they must be learned so that we can use the *Nautical Almanac* and the *Navigation Tables*.

They are the following: *Declination*, *Azimuth* and *Hour Angle* (with its three varieties).

Declination means, as far as we are concerned, nothing more than Latitude of K. When we want to find the latitude of K we must look for it in the *Nautical Almanac* under the heading "Declination" or, more simply, "Dec." Astronomers have a broader meaning for the term, but all that we have to remember is that Declination or Dec. at the head of a column means that the figures listed below give us the latitude of K.

Azimuth means *bearing* and, as ordinarily used, means the bearing of the star from the ship, or the bearing of K from either the ship or A. If we say that the Azimuth of K is 45° or that the Azimuth of K is N E, all that we mean is that K bears 45° from us, or N E from us.

Hour Angle (H. A.), sometimes called *Local Hour Angle* (L. H. A.), is the difference in longitudes of any two points. It can be expressed in either degrees or hours (since the earth turns through 360 degrees in 24 hours, 15° = 1 hour), but in navigation we use degrees.

The *Nautical Almanac* lists three special cases of Hour Angle.

1) *Greenwich Hour Angle* (G. H. A.) is the difference between any point and the longitude of Greenwich, England. Since this latter is, by international convention, 0°, the G. H. A. of any point is simply its longitude measured, as already mentioned, westward.

Thus in   Diagram 13 while the *Local Hour Angle* between P and M is 15° and between P and N is 70° the *Greenwich Hour Angles* of P, M, and N are 45°, 60°, and 335°.

2) *Aries* is a point in the sky somewhere in the Milky Way which has been chosen by astronomers, for reasons best known to them, as a point of reference, and is treated in the *Nautical Almanac* as a star.   It has, therefore, a Greenwich Hour Angle which is listed in the *Almanac* under the heading of GHA ♈ on the same pages as the GHAs of the sun, moon and planets.

3) *Sidereal Hour Angle* (S. H. A.).   This is the hour angle between *Aries* and any of the fixed stars and is, for practical purposes, invariable.

The SHAs and Declinations of the 57 brightest stars are listed in two columns on the inside front cover of the *Almanac*.

The S. H. A. of any star added to the G. H. A. of *Aries* (G. H. A. ♈) gives us the G. H. A. of that star.   This makes a small amount of extra work for us but saves a great deal of paper.

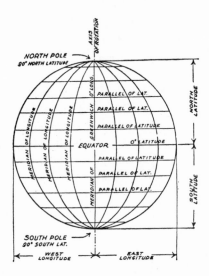

Equator is that great circle of the earth which lies midway between the poles. Every point on the Equator is 90° from either pole.

Parallels of Latitude are circles whose planes are parallel to the plane of the Equator. They have their centers in the axis of rotation and the radii vary from zero at either pole to that of the Equator. The Equator is the only parallel of latitude which is a great circle.

§14. Greenwich Mean Time of Observation

The Greenwich Hour Angle is obtained from the *Almanac* for Greenwich time of the observation, therefore upon taking your altitude you must read the chronometer and correct the reading to get true Greenwich time. Greenwich time is called Greenwich Mean Time in the *Almanac* and is frequently abbreviated to G. M. T.

Since your chronometer will very seldom read true G. M. T., it must be checked every day by radio time signals. If you can't get radio time signals you must check your chronometer whenever you are in port, either by the time from another boat or by time signals from shore, and you must also determine the rate of gain or loss per day since your last check.

If on May 2 the clock is 2 minutes 25 seconds fast and is losing 2 seconds per day, on May 10 it will be 2 minutes 09 seconds fast, and you must subtract 2 minutes, 09 seconds from your reading to get Greenwich Mean Time.

If you keep a small notebook and pencil in your chronometer case and enter the date and total correction every day when you wind the clock it will make your work easier.

To get the G. M. T. of your observation of altitude you must also subtract from your chronometer reading the number of seconds that have elapsed between the time of taking the altitude and reading the chronometer.

There are various schools of thought as to the best method of measuring this interval.

If you have a trained helper let him watch the chronometer and write down the reading the instant you shout, "Mark!" In this case the time interval will be 0 seconds.

If, for any reason, you have no assistant, you can time the interval with a stop watch, or you can simply count seconds from the moment you have found the altitude until you reach the chronometer. Anyone can learn to count seconds well enough for this purpose, if he keeps his chronometer in an accessible position so that the interval is not more than 10 or 15 seconds. His error in counting should not be more than a second or two, which would cause the longitude to be out no more than half a mile.

Greenwich Mean Time of Observation = Chronometer reading ± total error — time lapsed between sextant observation and chronometer reading.

This is the time to be used in looking up all data in the Nautical Almanac regardless of what ship's time may be.

§15. THE GREENWICH DATE

Another very important thing to keep in mind is that the date is always the Greenwich Date. For example, when you are taking evening star sights around New York in summer (Daylight Saving Time) you must remember that 9 P.M. on June 1 in New York is 2 A.M. on June 2 in Greenwich. So you would have to obtain your Declination and G. H. A. for June 2 and not June 1.

Greenwich Mean Time (G. M. T.) is given in the *Almanac* as A. M. and P. M. on consecutive pages.

Chapter III

§16. GREENWICH HOUR ANGLE OF A STAR

We will now take an example, showing how to use the *Nautical Almanac*.

On the morning of May 22, 1967, the altitude of *Regulus* was observed to be 26° 35′. The chronometer reading at this time was 7h. 31m. 10s. from which 2m. 28s. chronometer error is to be subtracted, giving G. M. T. of observation as 7h. 28m. 42s.

Dead Reckoning position is Lat. 43° 20′ N. Long. 47° 17′ W.

The main section of the *Nautical Almanac* is laid out with each pair of facing pages, (from 10 to 253) listing the G. H. A. and Dec. of Aries, the sun, moon, and planets for every hour of G. M. T. for three days. The yellow pages at the back of the book, (i to xxxi) entitled *Increments and Corrections*, give the number of degrees and minutes of arc to be added to the hourly G. H. A. according to the exact time of observation. The S. H. A. and Dec. of the fixed stars, which change very slowly, are listed in the right-hand columns of the even-numbered pages.

Now we can proceed. We turn to page 104 of the 1967 *Nautical Almanac* and find the S. H. A. of *Regulus* on May 22 to be 208°20.6′ (which we round off to 208° 21′) and its Dec. to be N 12° 08′.

The G. H. A. of *Aries* on May 22 at 7 A.M. is 344° 13′. But the exact time of the observarion was 7h 28m 42s so we turn to the yellow pages to find how much to add for the extra 28m 42s.   On page xvi we look down the left-hand section, headed 28m, along the column headed *Aries,* and opposite 42s we find the figure 7° 11.7′.   We add this 7° 12′ to 344° 13′ and find that G. H. A. *Aries* at the time of observation was 351° 25′.

G. H. A. *Regulus* equals S. H. A. *Regulus* plus G. H. A. *Aries* so

S. H. A. *Regulus*	208° 21′
G. H. A. *Aries*	351° 25′
G. H. A. *Regulus*	559° 46′

Since obviously we can subtract 360°, a whole circle, without changing the Hour Angle, we can say that G. H. A. *Regulus* is 199° 46′.

Our Dead Reckoning Longitude was 47° 17′ West and we must choose for our Assumed Point a longitude which will give us a local hour angle in whole degrees.   In this case it will be 47° 46′ and the local hour angle will be 199° 46′ minus 47° 46′, or 152°.

Summarizing   H. A. *Regulus*   152°
                        Dec. *Regulus*   N 12° 08′
                        Latitude A   43° N

With this information, obtained from the *Nautical Almanac,* we turn to the *Navigation Tables,* H. O. 214, and take out the Azimuth and Altitude of *Regulus* from the Assumed Point, compare the Observed and Calculated Altitudes and draw our Position Line.   (See §6).

A word about *Azimuth* is necessary.   The *Tables* give azimuth simply as a number between 0 and 180 and we must supply the N, E, S, and W by ourselves.   The rule for N or S is easy. If Lat. ship is N, azimuth is N.   If ship is S, azimuth is S.

The rule for E or W is a little more difficult.

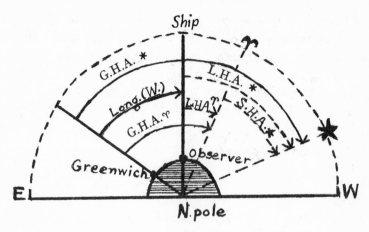

DIAGRAM 14.

The above diagram, showing the plane of the equator as seen from the north pole, illustrates the relationship between the Greenwich and local hour angles, and longitude and sidereal hour angle.

G. H. A. of *Aries* (♈), Sun, Moon and planets are tabulated directly; for these:

L. H. A. = G. H. A. − W. longitude (+ E. longitude)

For the stars:

G. H. A. ★ = G. H. A. ♈ + S. H. A. ★

L. H. A. ★ = L. H. A. ♈ + S. H. A. ★

L. H. A. ★ = G. H. A. ♈ + S. H. A. ★
      − W. longitude (+ E. longitude)

If Long. Ship is west, you *subtract Long. Ship from G. H. A.* This gives the number of degrees that K is west of the ship. (If G. H. A. is smaller than Long. Ship, you must add 360° to G. H. A.)

Then if the difference in longitudes (the hour angle) is less than 180°, the azimuth is W. If the difference is more than 180°, the azimuth is E.

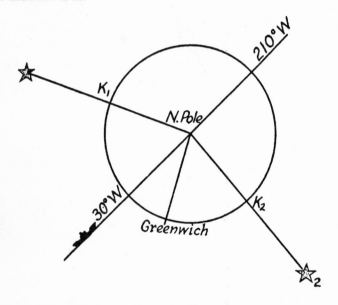

DIAGRAM 15.

If Long. Ship is E, you *add Long. Ship to G. H. A.* If the sum is less than 180°, the azimuth is W. If the sum is between 180° and 360°, the azimuth is E. (If the sum is more than 360°, subtract 360° and treat as above.)

Diagram 15 illustrates this point. All K's to the left of the 30°–210° line have hour angles relative to the ship of less than 180°. Likewise, to an observer on the ship, all these K's would have a westerly bearing. And, conversely, all K's with hour angles relative to the ship of more than 180° have an easterly bearing.

In the example just given, the azimuth is N . . . W, since D. R. Lat. is North and H. A. is less than 180°.

(The *Navigation Tables* do not list hour angles higher than 180°, so if the hour angle is more than 180° we subtract it from 360° and use the remainder *while working with the Tables*. Doing this will not affect the numerical value of the azimuth. You must remember, however, that the azimuth is still E.)

§18. We Get Down to Cases

Up till now this discussion has been on a pretty high plane with very little work involved. But it is the transition from the general to the particular which causes grief to navigators as well as to philosophers and airplane pilots, and this transition must now be made. In other words, we must get down to cases.

At present there are three standard books of navigation tables in general use. These are H. O. 208, H. O. 211 and H. O. 214.[*] The first two are thin volumes of 60- or 70-pages, which give all the needed information in condensed form, but require a certain amount of computation after hour angle, latitude and declination have been obtained.

H. O. 214, published in 1940 by the United States Hydrographic Office, comes in nine volumes, and requires practically no work at all. Each volume contains the data for 10 degrees of latitude of A. Volume I covers Lat. 0° to Lat. 10°, Volume II covers Lat. 10° to Lat. 20°, and so on.

*In the near future, H. O. 229 will replace H. O. 214.

Several pages of figures are given for each latitude. The vertical columns are headed by declinations for every half-degree from 0 to 90. The horizontal rows are headed by hour angles—every possible hour angle that can be observed from the latitude in question. The title across the top of the page tells whether the latitude and declination are of the same sign (both north or both south) or of opposite signs (one north and the other south).

All that you have to do, therefore, is to open the book at the proper page, look for the column headed by the declination closest to the declination of your star and follow down the column to the row for your *hour angle*. There you will find, already worked out (for the declination at the head of the column) the *altitude* and the *azimuth*. The only work that you have to do is to correct this altitude for the exact declination of your star.

This is very easily done. Next to the altitude is a small sign Δd, followed by a number. This number must be multiplied by the *difference* in declination between your star and the declination at the head of the column, and the product must be added to or subtracted from the altitude given in the tables.

Suppose you are looking up the star Procyon, which has a declination of 5° 22′. Find the column headed Declination 5° 30′. (See table inserted on pages 42–3.) Suppose your H. A. is 14°. Then the corresponding altitude is given as 50° 30′.6 and Δd is 96 (the decimal point in Δd is omitted in the tables). 8′ × .96 = 7′.7, which must be added to or subtracted from the 50° 30′.6 given in the table.

You find out whether to add or subtract by looking at the altitude given in the adjoining column (Declination 5° 00′) and seeing whether this is larger or smaller than 50° 30′.6.. If it is larger, add the 7′.7. If it is smaller, subtract the 7′.7. In the example just given, the 7′.7 must be subtracted.

The figure for the azimuth does not need to be corrected as it varies slowly, and all we need for plotting is the nearest degree.

If your ship has a copy of H. O. 214 you might never use any other tables although some marine navigators now use H. O. 249 (see p. 80). However, in case you have to use H. O. 208 or H. O. 211, a few notes on them are included in Chapter IX.

There is one thing to mention. You know that the intercept is found by subtracting the distance ship-K from the distance A-K. But since *distance* is simply 5400′ − altitude, you will get the same numerical value for the Intercept if you subtract Altitude observed from ship from *altitude which would have been observed if the ship had been at A*. The latter is called the *calculated altitude*, and is recorded in the tables instead of the calculated distance. Therefore to get your intercept you have only to subtract true altitude from calculated altitude.

The nearer you are to K the higher the star appears above the horizon, therefore if true altitude is *greater* than calculated altitude, lay off the intercept TOWARD K, while if true altitude is less than calculated altitude you lay off the intercept AWAY from K.

§19. THE COMPLETE PROBLEM

Now we may go through one complete problem and see how it is worked.

On the morning of January 1, 1953, an observation of *Procyon* was taken from the ship *Avedis*. D. R. Lat. 43° 12′ N., Long. 60° 15′ W. Observed altitude was 12° 34′; height of eye, 25 feet; index error +2′. Chronometer reading 10h. 10m. 32s; its error 2m. 32s. fast.

Draw the position line.

First we find G. M. T. (Greenwich Mean Time) of the observation by subtracting the correction from the chronometer reading, which gives us G. M. T. Jan. 1, 10h. 8m. 0s.

Then we turn to the *Nautical Almanac* and look up *Procyon*. The star's declination is given as N 5° 20.8′, and its sidereal hour angle (S. H. A.) as 245° 46.8′.

The Greenwich Hour Angle (G. H. A.) of ♈ for 10h. of G. M. T., as indicated on extreme left of page, is 250° 45.5′. But since the observation was taken at 10h. 8m. 0s., we also must enter the *Increments & Correction Tables* (yellow pages) under the *8m.* heading and abreast of *0s.*, and obtain 2° 00.3′ as the correction. G. H. A. of ♈ for time of observation, therefore, is 252° 45.8′. This value is added to the star's S. H. A. and we get as G. H. A. of *Procyon* 498° 32.6′ at G. M. T. of observation. However, since there are 360 degrees in the circle, we may, as previously noted, add or subtract full circles without altering an hour angle. So we subtract 360° from 498° 32.6′ and get 138° 32.6′.

Now we are ready to choose our assumed position A.

Our D. R. longitude is 60° 15′ W. Our G. H. A. is 138° 32.6′, which we may call 138° 33′. Therefore our assumed longitude is 60° 33′ W. and our H. A. is 138° 33′ − 60° 33′ = 78°.

Our D. R. latitude is 43° 12′ N.; therefore our assumed latitude is 43° N. (See §11)

We now look in Volume V of H. O. 214 and turn to page 82 (Latitude and Declination of same name). We look down the column headed "Dec. +5° 30′" to the row headed "H. A. 78°".

There we see Alt. 12° 31'; d=68; Az. 94.2°. Difference in Declinations (§18) is 30—21=9'. 9'×.68=6.12'. So 6' must be subtracted from the listed altitude because Alt. at Dec. 5° 00' is 12° 10.6', which is smaller than 12° 31'. Our calculated altitude is, therefore, 12° 25'. The azimuth is read directly as 94.2°.

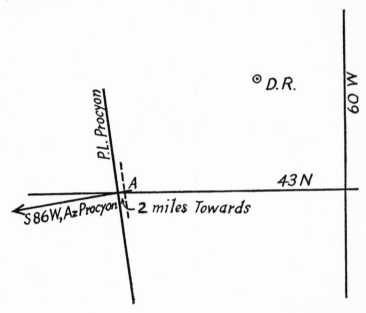

DIAGRAM 16.

According to rule, azimuth takes the sign of the latitude. So, since the ship is in the northern hemisphere, the azimuth is N 94°. In order to determine whether it is N 94° E or N 94° W, we must remember that hour angles of less than 180° have a west azimuth. (See §16.) The hour angle in this case is 78°, which

DECLINATION SAME NAME AS LATITUDE

Lat. 43°

Each declination cell lists: Alt. | Δd Δt Az.

H.A.	4° 00′	4° 30′	5° 00′	5° 30′	6° 00′	6° 30′	7° 00′	7° 30′	H.A.
00	51 00.0 1.00 1.00 180.0	51 30.0 1.00 1.00 180.0	52 00.0 1.00 1.00 180.0	52 30.0 1.00 1.00 180.0	53 00.0 1.00 1.00 180.0	53 30.0 1.00 1.00 180.0	54 00.0 1.00 1.00 180.0	54 30.0 1.00 1.00 180.0	00
1	50 59.4 1.00 1.03 178.4	51 29.4 1.00 1.03 178.4	51 59.4 1.00 1.03 178.6	52 29.4 1.00 1.03 178.4	52 59.4 1.00 1.03 178.3	53 29.4 1.00 1.03 178.3	53 59.4 1.00 1.03 178.3	54 29.3 1.00 1.03 178.3	1
2	50 57.6 1.00 1.05 176.8	51 27.5 1.00 1.05 176.8	51 57.5 1.00 1.05 176.9	52 27.5 1.00 1.05 176.7	52 57.5 1.00 1.05 176.7	53 27.5 1.00 1.05 176.6	53 57.4 1.00 1.05 176.6	54 27.4 1.00 1.05 176.6	2
3	50 54.5 1.00 1.07 175.3	51 24.5 1.00 1.07 175.2	51 54.4 1.00 1.07 175.2	52 24.4 1.00 1.07 175.0	52 54.3 1.00 1.07 175.0	53 24.2 1.00 1.07 175.0	53 54.2 1.00 1.06 174.9	54 24.1 1.00 1.06 174.9	3
4	50 50.3 1.00 1.09 173.7	51 20.2 1.00 1.09 173.7	51 50.1 1.00 1.09 173.5	52 20.0 1.00 1.09 173.5	52 49.9 1.00 1.09 173.5	53 19.8 1.00 1.09 173.4	53 49.7 1.00 1.08 173.3	54 19.6 1.00 1.08 173.2	4
05	50 44.9 99 11 172.1	51 14.7 99 11 172.0	51 44.6 99 11 172.0	52 14.4 99 11 171.6	52 44.2 99 12 171.7	53 14.1 99 12 171.6	53 43.9 99 12 171.6	54 13.7 99 12 171.5	05
6	50 38.3 99 13 170.5	51 08.0 99 13 170.4	51 37.8 99 13 170.5	52 07.6 99 13 170.3	52 37.3 99 14 170.1	53 07.1 99 14 170.1	53 36.8 99 14 169.9	54 06.6 99 14 169.8	6
7	50 30.4 99 15 169.0	51 00.2 99 15 168.9	51 29.8 99 15 168.8	51 59.5 99 15 168.6	52 29.2 99 16 168.5	52 58.9 99 16 168.5	53 28.6 99 16 168.3	53 58.2 99 16 168.1	7
8	50 21.5 99 17 167.4	50 51.1 99 17 167.4	51 21.0 99 17 167.3	51 50.3 99 17 167.2	52 19.9 99 18 166.9	52 49.5 99 18 166.8	53 19.0 99 18 166.6	53 48.6 99 18 166.5	8
9	50 11.4 99 19 165.9	50 40.9 99 19 165.8	51 10.4 99 19 165.6	51 39.9 99 19 165.5	52 09.3 99 20 165.3	52 38.8 99 20 165.2	53 08.3 99 20 165.0	53 37.7 99 20 164.8	9
10	50 00.1 98 21 164.1	50 29.5 98 21 164.2	50 58.9 98 21 164.1	51 23.3 98 21 163.6	51 57.6 98 21 163.7	52 27.0 98 22 163.6	52 56.3 98 22 163.4	53 25.6 98 22 163.2	10
11	49 47.7 98 22 162.5	50 17.0 98 22 162.7	50 46.3 98 23 162.5	51 15.5 98 23 162.3	51 44.8 98 23 162.2	52 12.4 98 24 162.0	52 43.2 98 24 161.8	53 12.4 98 24 161.6	11
12	49 34.3 98 24 161.0	50 03.4 98 25 161.2	50 32.5 98 25 161.0	51 01.6 98 25 160.6	51 30.7 98 25 160.4	51 59.8 98 25 160.4	52 28.9 98 25 160.2	52 57.9 98 25 160.0	12
13	49 19.6 98 25 159.5	49 48.7 98 25 159.7	50 17.7 98 27 159.3	50 46.6 98 27 159.3	51 15.6 98 27 159.1	51 44.5 98 27 158.8	52 13.4 98 27 158.6	52 42.3 98 26 158.4	13
14	49 04.0 98 28 158.4	49 32.9 98 26 158.2	50 01.7 98 28 158.0	50 30.6 98 29 157.8	50 59.4 98 29 157.5	51 28.1 98 29 157.3	51 56.9 98 29 157.1	52 25.6 98 30 156.8	14
15	48 47.3 96 30 156.9	49 16.1 96 30 156.7	49 44.7 96 30 156.5	50 13.4 96 30 156.3	50 42.1 96 31 155.5	51 10.7 96 31 155.4	51 39.3 96 31 155.5	52 07.8 96 31 155.3	15
16	48 29.6 95 31 155.5	48 58.2 95 31 155.3	49 26.7 95 32 155.0	49 55.2 95 32 154.8	50 23.7 95 32 154.4	50 52.2 95 33 154.2	51 20.6 95 33 154.0	51 48.9 95 33 153.8	16
17	48 10.9 95 33 154.0	48 39.3 95 33 153.8	49 07.7 95 33 153.6	49 36.0 95 34 153.1	50 04.7 95 34 153.1	50 32.6 95 34 152.9	51 00.8 95 34 152.5	51 29.0 95 34 152.3	17
18	47 51.2 94 34 152.7	48 19.5 94 34 152.4	48 47.7 94 34 152.1	49 15.8 94 35 151.9	49 44.0 94 36 151.6	50 12.0 94 36 151.4	50 40.1 94 36 151.1	51 08.1 93 37 150.8	18
19	47 30.6 93 36 151.3	47 58.7 94 36 151.0	48 26.7 94 37 150.8	48 54.7 94 37 150.4	49 22.6 94 37 150.2	49 50.3 94 37 149.9	50 18.4 94 38 149.6	50 46.2 93 38 149.3	19
20	47 09.9 93 37 149.9	47 36.9 93 38 149.6	48 04.8 93 38 149.3	48 32.6 93 38 149.1	49 00.3 93 39 148.8	49 28.0 93 39 148.5	49 55.7 92 39 148.2	50 23.3 92 40 147.9	20
1	46 46.6 92 39 148.3	47 14.3 92 39 148.3	47 41.9 92 40 148.0	48 09.5 92 40 147.7	48 37.1 92 40 147.4	49 04.6 92 40 147.1	49 32.1 92 41 146.8	49 59.5 91 41 146.4	1
2	46 23.2 92 40 147.2	46 50.8 92 41 146.9	47 18.2 92 41 146.6	47 45.6 91 41 146.4	48 13.0 92 41 146.0	48 40.3 92 42 145.7	49 07.6 92 42 145.4	49 34.8 91 43 145.1	2
3	45 59.1 91 42 145.6	46 26.4 91 42 145.6	46 53.7 91 42 145.3	47 20.9 91 43 145.0	47 48.1 91 43 144.7	48 15.2 91 43 144.3	48 42.2 91 44 144.0	49 09.3 90 44 143.7	3
4	45 34.0 91 43 144.3	46 01.2 91 43 144.3	46 28.2 91 44 143.8	46 55.3 91 44 143.6	47 22.3 91 44 143.3	47 49.2 91 45 142.9	48 16.0 90 45 142.7	48 42.9 90 45 142.3	4
25	45 08.2 90 45 142.7	45 35.1 90 45 142.0	46 02.0 90 45 142.7	46 28.9 90 45 142.3	46 55.6 90 46 142.0	47 22.4 89 46 141.7	47 49.0 90 46 141.3	48 15.6 88 46 141.0	25
6	44 41.6 90 46 141.0	45 08.3 89 46 141.7	45 35.0 89 46 141.0	46 01.7 89 47 141.1	46 28.4 89 47 140.7	46 54.8 88 47 140.4	47 21.2 88 48 140.0	47 47.6 88 48 139.7	6
7	44 14.2 89 47 140.5	44 40.8 88 47 140.5	45 07.3 89 47 140.1	45 33.7 88 48 139.8	46 00.1 88 48 139.5	46 26.4 88 48 139.1	46 52.7 87 49 138.7	47 18.9 87 49 138.8	7
8	43 46.1 88 48 139.2	44 12.5 88 48 139.2	44 38.8 88 49 138.9	45 05.0 88 49 138.6	45 31.2 88 50 138.2	45 57.3 87 50 137.9	46 23.4 87 50 137.5	46 49.4 87 50 137.1	8
9	43 17.3 89 49 138.0	43 43.5 87 49 138.0	44 09.6 87 50 137.7	44 35.6 87 50 137.3	45 01.6 87 50 137.0	45 27.5 86 51 136.6	45 53.4 86 51 136.3	46 19.2 86 51 135.9	9
30	42 47.8 87 50 136.8	43 13.8 87 51 136.8	43 39.7 86 51 136.5	44 05.6 86 51 136.1	44 31.4 86 52 135.8	44 57.1 85 52 135.4	45 22.7 85 52 135.0	45 48.3 85 53 134.7	30
1	42 17.7 86 51 135.5	42 43.4 86 52 135.7	43 09.0 85 52 135.5	43 34.8 85 52 135.0	44 00.4 85 53 134.6	44 25.9 85 53 134.1	44 51.0 85 53 133.7	45 16.8 84 54 133.5	1
2	41 46.9 85 52 134.5	42 12.5 85 53 134.5	42 38.0 85 53 134.1	43 03.5 85 53 133.8	43 28.9 85 54 133.4	43 54.2 84 54 133.1	44 18.9 84 54 132.6	44 44.6 84 55 132.3	2
3	41 15.5 85 53 133.7	41 40.9 85 53 133.7	42 06.2 84 54 133.0	42 31.5 84 54 132.6	42 56.7 84 55 132.2	43 21.8 84 55 131.9	43 46.5 84 55 131.1	44 11.9 83 56 131.1	3
4	40 43.4 84 54 132.6	41 08.7 84 55 132.7	41 33.8 84 55 131.9	41 58.9 84 55 131.5	42 23.9 84 56 131.1	42 48.9 83 56 130.8	43 13.7 83 56 130.0	43 38.5 82 56 130.0	4
35	40 10.9 84 55 131.5	40 35.9 83 56 131.1	41 00.9 83 56 131.0	41 25.8 83 57 130.4	41 50.6 83 57 130.1	42 15.4 82 57 129.6	42 40.6 82 57 128.9	43 04.6 82 57 128.9	35
6	39 37.7 83 56 130.4	40 02.6 83 56 130.1	40 27.4 83 57 129.7	40 52.1 82 57 129.3	41 16.7 82 58 128.9	41 41.3 82 58 128.6	42 05.9 81 58 127.8	42 30.2 81 58 127.8	6
7	39 04.1 82 57 129.4	39 28.7 82 57 129.0	39 53.3 82 58 128.6	40 17.9 82 58 128.2	40 42.3 81 58 127.9	41 06.7 81 58 127.7	41 31.0 80 59 126.7	41 55.3 81 59 126.7	7
8	38 29.9 82 58 128.3	38 54.4 82 58 127.9	39 18.8 81 58 127.6	39 43.2 81 59 127.2	40 07.4 81 59 126.9	40 31.7 80 59 126.4	40 55.8 80 60 125.6	41 19.8 80 60 125.6	8
9	37 55.2 81 59 127.3	38 19.5 81 59 126.9	38 43.8 81 59 126.5	39 08.0 81 59 126.1	39 32.1 80 60 125.8	39 56.1 80 60 125.4	40 20.1 79 61 124.6	40 43.9 79 61 124.5	9
40	37 20.0 81 59 126.2	37 44.2 80 60 125.6	38 08.3 80 60 125.5	38 32.3 80 60 125.5	38 56.2 80 60 124.7	39 20.1 79 61 124.3	39 43.9 79 61 123.5	40 07.6 79 61 123.4	40
1	36 44.4 80 60 125.2	37 08.4 80 60 124.9	37 32.3 80 61 124.1	37 56.2 79 61 124.1	38 20.0 79 61 123.7	38 43.6 79 61 123.3	39 07.3 78 62 122.5	39 30.8 78 62 122.5	1
2	36 08.4 80 61 124.3	36 32.2 79 61 123.9	36 55.9 79 62 123.5	37 19.6 79 62 123.1	37 43.2 79 62 122.7	38 06.8 78 62 122.3	38 30.2 78 62 121.7	38 53.6 78 63 121.9	2

A numerical traverse/trigonometric table. Row index values run down both margins:

3 4 | 45 6 7 8 9 | 50 1 2 3 4 | 55 6 7 8 9 | 60 1 2 3 4 | 65 6 7 8 9 | 70 1 2 3 4 | 75 6 7 8 9 | 80 1 2 3 4 | 85 6 7 8 9 | 90

3 4	35 31.9 / 35 55.0	35 55.6 / 35 18.5	36 19.2 / 35 42.0	36 42.7 / 36 05.3	37 06.1 / 36 28.6	37 29.5 / 36 51.8	37 52.8 / 37 15.0	38 16.0 / 37 38.0		3 4
45	34 17.7	34 41.1	35 04.4	35 27.6	35 50.7	36 13.8	36 36.8	36 59.7	120.5 / 119.6	45
6	33 40.1	34 03.3	34 26.4	34 49.5	35 12.5	35 35.4	35 58.2	36 21.0	121.4 / 120.4	6
7	33 02.1	33 25.1	34 48.1	34 11.0	35 12.5 / 33.3	34 56.7	35 19.4	36 42.0	118.6 / 118.7	7
8	32 23.7	32 46.6	33 09.5	33 32.3	35 55.0	34 17.6	34 40.2	35 02.6	117.7 / 116.8	8
9	31 45.0	32 07.8	33 30.5	33 53.2	33 15.7	34 38.2	34 00.6	34 23.0	115.9 / 115.0	9
50	31 06.0	31 28.7	31 51.2	32 13.8	32 36.2	32 58.6	33 20.8	33 43.1	114.1	50
1	30 26.7	30 49.2	31 11.7	31 34.1	32 56.4	32 18.6	32 40.8	33 02.9	113.0	1
2	29 47.1	30 09.5	31 31.8	31 54.1	31 16.3	31 38.4	32 00.4	32 22.4	112.3	2
3	29 07.2	29 29.5	29 51.7	30 13.8	30 35.9	30 57.9	31 19.8	31 41.7	111.5	3
4	28 27.1	28 49.1	29 11.3	30 33.3	29 55.3	30 17.2	30 39.0	31 00.7	110.6	4
55	27 46.6	28 08.7	28 30.7	28 52.6	29 14.4	29 36.2	29 57.9	30 19.6	109.8	55
6	27 06.0	27 27.9	27 49.8	28 11.6	28 33.4	28 55.0	29 16.6	29 38.2	109.0	6
7	26 25.1	26 46.9	27 08.7	27 30.4	27 52.1	28 13.6	28 35.1	28 56.6	108.2	7
8	25 44.0	26 05.7	27 27.4	26 49.0	27 10.6	27 32.0	27 53.4	28 14.8	107.4	8
9	25 02.7	25 24.3	25 45.9	26 07.4	26 28.9	26 50.2	27 11.6	27 32.8	106.6	9
60	24 21.2	24 42.7	25 04.2	25 25.6	25 47.0	26 08.3	26 29.5	26 50.7	105.8	60
1	23 39.5	24 00.9	24 22.2	24 43.6	25 04.9	25 26.1	26 17.2	26 08.3	105.0	1
2	22 57.6	23 19.0	23 40.3	24 01.5	24 22.7	25 43.8	25 04.9	25 25.9	104.2	2
3	22 15.5	22 36.8	22 58.0	23 19.2	23 40.3	24 01.4	24 22.4	24 43.3	103.5	3
4	21 33.3	21 54.5	22 15.7	22 36.7	23 57.8	23 18.8	23 39.7	24 00.5	102.7	4
65	20 50.9	21 12.1	21 33.1	21 54.1	22 15.1	22 36.0	22 56.9	23 17.7	102.0	65
6	20 08.4	20 29.5	20 50.5	21 11.4	21 32.3	21 53.2	22 13.9	22 34.7	101.2	6
7	19 25.7	19 46.7	20 07.7	20 28.6	20 49.4	21 10.2	21 30.9	21 51.6	100.5	7
8	18 43.0	19 03.9	19 24.8	20 45.6	20 06.4	20 27.1	20 47.8	21 08.4	99.7	8
9	18 00.0	18 20.9	18 41.7	19 02.5	19 23.2	19 43.9	20 04.5	20 25.1	99.0	9
70	17 17.0	17 37.8	17 58.6	18 19.3	19 40.0	19 00.6	19 21.2	19 41.7	98.3	70
1	16 33.9	16 54.6	17 15.4	18 36.0	17 56.6	18 17.2	18 37.8	18 58.3	97.6	1
2	15 50.7	16 11.4	16 32.0	16 52.7	17 13.2	17 33.8	17 54.3	18 14.7	96.9	2
3	15 07.3	15 28.0	16 48.6	16 09.2	16 29.7	16 50.2	17 10.7	17 31.1	96.2	3
4	14 23.9	14 44.6	15 05.1	15 25.7	15 46.2	16 06.7	16 27.1	16 47.5	95.4	4
75	13 40.5	14 01.0	14 21.6	14 42.1	15 02.6	15 23.0	15 43.4	16 03.8	94.7	75
6	12 56.9	13 17.4	13 38.0	13 58.4	14 18.9	14 39.3	14 59.7	15 20.0	94.1	6
7	12 13.3	12 33.8	12 54.3	13 14.7	13 35.2	13 55.5	14 15.9	14 36.2	93.4	7
8	11 29.6	11 50.1	12 10.6	12 31.0	13 51.4	13 11.8	13 32.1	13 52.4	92.7	8
9	10 45.9	11 06.4	11 26.8	11 47.2	12 07.6	12 27.9	12 48.3	13 08.5	92.0	9
80	10 02.1	10 22.6	10 43.0	11 03.4	11 23.8	11 44.1	12 04.4	12 24.7	91.3	80
1	9 18.3	9 38.8	9 59.2	10 19.6	10 39.9	11 00.2	11 20.5	11 40.8	90.6	1
2	8 34.5	8 54.9	9 15.3	9 35.7	9 56.0	10 16.3	10 36.7	10 56.9	89.9	2
3	7 50.7	8 11.1	8 31.5	8 51.8	9 12.2	9 32.5	9 52.8	10 13.1	89.2	3
4	7 06.8	7 27.2	7 47.6	8 07.9	8 28.3	8 48.6	9 08.9	9 29.2	88.6	4
85	6 22.9	6 43.3	7 03.7	7 24.1	7 44.4	8 04.7	8 25.0	8 45.3	87.9	85
6	5 39.1	5 59.4	6 19.8	6 40.2	7 00.5	7 20.9	7 41.2	8 01.5	87.2	6
7		5 15.6	5 36.0	5 56.3	6 16.7	6 37.0	6 57.4	7 17.7	86.5	7
8				5 12.5	5 32.9	5 53.2	6 13.6	6 33.9	85.9	8
9						5 09.4	5 29.8	5 50.1	85.2	9
90								5 06.4	84.5	90

means that K is 78° W of the ship and therefore the azimuth is N 94 W.

We now have all the information needed to draw a position line through our assumed position.

Lat. A is 43° N; Long. A is 60° 33′ W. The bearing from A

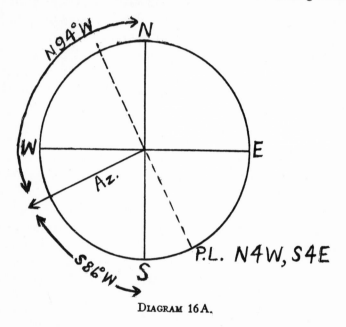

DIAGRAM 16A.

to K is N 94 W which is the same as S 86 W. We can prick off the position of A on our chart, and draw through it a line bearing N 4 W (shown as dotted line in Diagram 16) which is at right angles to the azimuth. This is the position line of A.

The only thing left to do is to find the intercept (§7), which, as you may remember, is the difference between the calculated altitude and the true altitude.

To get the true altitude we must correct the sextant altitude for height of eye above sea level, index error, and refraction.

The tables for these corrections are on the front inside cover of *Nautical Almanac*. Correction for height of eye 25′ is —4.9′.

The correction for refraction depends on the observed altitude. Look in the table for corrections to be applied to observed altitude of a *star*. H_o is the observed altitude, and parallel to it, in the next column, is the correction to be applied. This correction is always subtracted in the case of a star, and added in the case of the sun (lower limb).

We look alongside H_o12 and find —4.3′.

Now we have the three corrections: —4.3′ (refraction) —4.9′ (height of eye +2′(index error) = —7.2′. We subtract 7′ (this is close enough) from our observed altitude of 12° 34′ and have for the true altitude 12° 27′.

Our calculated altitude was 12° 25′, therefore the intercept is 2′. Since the true altitude is greater than the calculated altitude, we lay off the intercept 2 miles TOWARD K along the line of bearing. Through this point we draw a line parallel to the position line through A, and this is the position line of our ship. (See Diagram 16.)

PROBLEMS

Choosing the Assumed Position.

Latitude A is the nearest whole degree to dead reckoning latitude.

Longitude A is nearest to the dead reckoning longitude that will give hour angle in whole degrees.

Hour angle is Greenwich hour angle of Star — west longitude of A (or + east longitude of A). (*Also see* HOUR ANGLE, *page 91.*)

1)

D. R. Lat.	25° 47′ N
D. R. Long.	45° 19′ W
G. H. A.	221° 42′

What is the assumed position and the hour angle?

Ans.   Lat. A   26° N
Long. A   45° 42′ W
H. A.   176°

2)

D. R. Lat.	25° 12′ S
D. R. Long.	147° 32′ E
G. H. A.	152° 24′

What is the assumed position and the hour angle?

Ans.   Lat. A   25° S
Long. A   147° 36′ E
H. A.   300° (or 60° E)

3)

D. R. Lat.	50° 29′ N
D. R. Long.	25° 18′ W

Observation of Aldebaran at 8h 32m 40s G. M. T., Jan. 17, 1953. What is the assumed position and hour angle?

S. H. A. *Aldebaran,* Jan. 17, 1953,   291° 41.2′
G. H. A. γ at 8h. G. M. T.   236° 26.8′
     correction for 32m 40s   + 8° 11.3′
                                                            ―――――――――
                                                             536° 19.3′
                                                            ―360°
                                                            ―――――――――
G. H. A. *Aldebaran* at observation   176° 19.3′

Ans. Lat. A 50° N. Long. A 25° 19′ W. H. A. 151°.

Problems in Sextant Corrections

True altitude = sextant altitude ± correction for altitude ± correction for height of eye ± index error

(The correction for altitude is + for the sun and − for the stars. The correction for height of eye is always − in H. O. 214 and H. O. 211. H. O. 208 uses 35 ft. as a base, therefore, for height of eye below 35 ft., the correction is +, above that it is −.)

1)

Sextant altitude of sun	42°
Index error	−2′
Height of eye	40 ft.

Corrections to be applied to the observed altitude of the sun						Correction for height of eye		Corrections to be applied to the observed altitude of a star					
H. E. ft.	Ho ° '	Sun's Corr. (+)	H. E. ft.	Ho ° '	Sun's Corr. (+)	Ht. of eye (ft)	Corr. (−) '	H.E. ft.	Ho ° '	Star's Corr. (−)	H. E. ft.	Ho ° '	Star's Corr. (−) '
		° '		26	+14.1		'			° '		26	−2.0
				27	14.2	10	− 3.1					27	1.9
	3	+ 1.6		28	14.3	12	3.4					28	1.8
	4	4.3		29	14.4	14	3.7					29	1.7
	5	6.3		30	14.4	16	3.9					30	1.7
	6	+ 7.7		31	+14.5	18	− 4.1		6	−8.5		31	−1.6
	7	8.7		32	14.6	20	4.4		7	7.4		32	1.6
	8	9.6		33	14.6	25	4.9		8	6.6		33	1.5
	9	10.3		34	14.7	30	5.4		9	5.9		34	1.4
	10	10.8		35	14.7	35	5.8		10	5.3		35	1.4
	11	+11.3		36	+14.8	40	− 6.2		11	−4.9		36	−1.3
	12	11.7		38	14.9	45	6.6		12	4.5		38	1.3
	13	12.0		40	15.0	50	6.9		13	4.1		40	1.2
	14	12.3		42	15.0	55	7.3		14	3.8		42	1.1
	15	12.6		44	15.1	60	7.6		15	3.6		44	1.0
	16	+12.8		45	+15.1	70	− 8.2		16	−3.4		45	−1.0
	17	13.0		50	15.3	80	8.8		17	3.1		50	0.8
	18	13.2		55	15.4	90	9.3		18	3.0		55	0.7
	19	13.3		60	15.5	100	9.8		19	2.8		60	0.6
	20	13.5		65	15.6	200	13.9		20	2.6		65	0.5
	21	+13.6		70	+15.7	300	−17.0		21	−2.5		70	−0.4
	22	13.7		75	15.8	400	19.6		22	2.4		75	0.3
	23	13.9		80	15.8	600	24.0		23	2.3		80	0.2
	24	14.0		85	15.9	800	27.7		24	2.2		85	0.1
	25	14.1		90	16.0	1000	31.0		25	2.1		90	0.0

NOTE.—In the blank left-hand columns above, the navigator may enter in pencil the correction for the height of eye most commonly used by him, thus saving himself one mental operation.

SEXTANT CORRECTION TABLE FROM H. O. 211 (Ageton).

True altitude is $42° + 15'$ (from table) $− 6'.2$ (from table) $− 2'$ (index error).

Ans. 42° 6'.8

2)   Sextant altitude of star   57° 30'
         Index error   +3'
         Height of eye   25 ft.
What is true altitude?
         Ans. 57° 27'.4

3)   Sextant altitude of sun   21° 43'
         Index error   −4'
         Height of eye   43 ft.
What is true altitude?
         Ans. 21° 46'.3

ALTITUDE AND AZIMUTH PROBLEMS
(Navigation tables are needed to solve these problems)

Problems in finding altitude and azimuth when latitude A, declination, and hour angle have been determined.

1)
Lat. A	25° S
Declination Acamar	−40° 30'
Hour angle	42°°

What is the calculated altitude and azimuth?
Declination and latitude are of same signs. Hour angle is between 0° and 180°, therefore azimuth is W. The sign of the azimuth is the sign of the latitude, therefore azimuth is S.

Ans. Alt. 51° 52'   Az. S55°.5W

2)
Lat. A	18° N
Declination Diphda	−18° 15'
Hour angle	23°

What is the calculated altitude and azimuth?
Ans. Alt. 47° 16.5'   Az. N 147° W which is S 33° W

3)
Lat. A	37° N
Declination Hamal	+23° 15'
Hour angle	2°

What is the calculated altitude and azimuth?
Ans. Alt. 76° 09'   Az. N 172° W or S 8° W

4)
Lat. A	5° N
Declination Alpheratz	+28° 50'
Hour angle	55°

What is the calculated altitude and azimuth?
Ans. Alt. 32° 51.5'   Az. N 58° .7' W

5)
Lat. A	55° N
Declination Marfak	+49° 39.6'
Hour angle	324°

What is the calculated altitude and azimuth?
Use H. A. 36 = (360 − 324). The Azimuth is east.
Ans. Alt. 67° 39'   Az. N 88°.7' E

6)
Lat. A	9° N
Declination Canopus	−52° 40'
Hour angle	44°

What is the calculated altitude and azimuth?
Ans. Alt. 17° 51'   Az. N 153°.6' W or S 26°.4' W

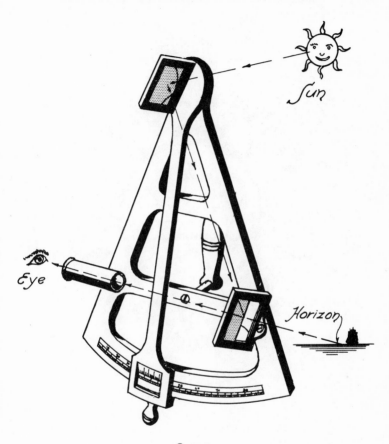

Octant

Showing three methods of marking compass cards.

FINDING THE POSITION LINE
Summary of Steps

Correct sextant altitude for height of
eye, index error, and altitude
(§ 10) .... *True Altitude*

•

Correct chronometer reading (§ 14) .... G. M.T.

•

Get G. H. A. for G. M. T. of observa-
tion (§ 16) ....G. H. A.

•

Get Lat. A and Long. A (§ 11)
Subtract Long. A from G.H.A. (§ 16).................... *Hour Angle*

•

Enter Tables with hour angle, Lat. A,
and declination. Take out .... *Calc. Alt.* and
(§ 18)   AZIMUTH

•

Note difference of *True Altitude* from
Calculated Altitude (§ 8) ....INTERCEPT

•

Draw line of AZIMUTH through A,
lay off INTERCEPT *toward* or *away.*
At right angles to AZIMUTH draw .... **POSITION LINE**
(§ 8)

• • •

Chapter IV

§20. NAVIGATING BY THE SUN

I have not mentioned navigation by the sun yet because it is only a special case of navigating by the stars and gives only one line of position, of course, at any instant. However, you often need a position in the daytime, and must use the sun. Also, it is easier to take the sun's altitude than a star's altitude when the weather is very rough or when it is hazy or cloudy. So you must know how to find your position by the sun, even though if you can get the stars it is much better to use them.

We get our position line from the altitude in exactly the same way that we do when we use a star, except that we have to use the Sun Tables in the *Almanac* to get the Greenwich hour angle. But, since there is only one sun, we cannot get an intersection right away. We have to wait until the sun has moved into a new position which will give us a good intersection. It is best to get position lines which cross at an angle of not less than 30 degrees, because if the lines are nearly parallel the position of the intersection is not definite and a small error in altitude will be magnified. (See Diagram 17.)

The sun moves through 15 degrees in an hour so we must wait about 2 hours between shots. But while the sun is moving the ship is moving too, and a position line made in one spot cannot be crossed with a position line made in a different spot. In the case of the stars, you get your shots a couple of minutes apart, and the distance traveled by the ship in that short time is negligible. But we cannot overlook 2 hours.

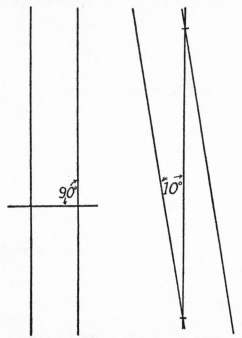

DIAGRAM 17. (*Left*) ONE MINUTE ERROR IN ALTITUDE MAKES ONE MILE ERROR IN POSITION. (*Right*) ONE MINUTE ERROR IN ALTITUDE MAKES SIX MILES ERROR IN POSITION.

So, to get the intersection we must advance the earlier position line in accordance with the distance traveled by the ship. This is done as follows: We take a shot at 9 A.M. (ship's time) and plot the position line, marking it P. L. 9 A.M. Then we keep track of the course and speed, and at 11 A.M., when we are ready to shoot the sun again, we know about how many miles we have come since 9 A.M., and in which direction. Suppose we have come 10 miles N E. Now we can say that *any* point on the line has advanced 10 miles N E since 9 A.M., therefore, *every* point has

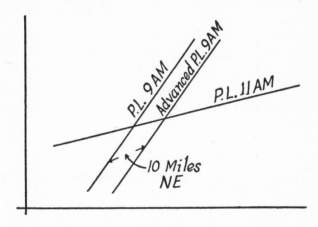

DIAGRAM 18.

advanced the same amount. So we can move the whole line 10 miles N E and call it the Advanced position line.

We now shoot the sun again and get an 11 A.M. position line which is crossed with the Advanced 9 A.M. line to give the position. (See Diagram 18.)

You can see from this that errors are likely to occur because even if you are certain of your mileage through the water you still cannot be sure how currents are affecting your position. So you never know if your position line has been advanced the correct amount and direction and consequently you are always uncertain as to your exact position.

If your two shots are taken close together you don't get a good cut; and if they are far apart the chance of error in advanc-

ing the position line is increased. So there is always some un-
certainty about the whole affair, and for this reason it is much
better to shoot the stars when you can.

In shooting the sun the *lower* limb should always be brought in
contact with the horizon.

Following is an example of determining line of position by an
altitude of the Sun, using H. O. 214.

April 8, 1953, in D. R. Lat. 43° 15′ N, Long. 160° 15′ W.
Obs. alt. Sun's lower limb (H_s) 28° 30′; height of eye 40 feet.
Chron. time 6h. 50m. 18s.; slow of G. M. T. 3m. 12s. Find calcu-
lated altitude and azimuth.

(Here we note that, since G. M. T. is 10h. 41m. *ahead* of time
of ship's meridian, the sight must have been taken about 8 a.m.,
which means that 12h. must be added to time shown by chronometer.)

Chron.	18h. 50m. 18s.	H_s	28° 30′
slow	+ 3 12	Ht. of eye	− 6′
		Corr.	+14′
G. M. T. April 8,	18 53 30		
		H_o Sun	28° 38′

From *Nautical Almanac:*

Sun's G. H. A. April 8, 18h.,   89° 32.5′ Dec. +7° 18.2′

corr. for 53m. 30s.	+ 13° 22.5′
G. H. A. at obs.	102° 55′
Assumed Long.	159° 55′W.
Sun's H. A.	−57° 00′
Add	360°
H. A.	303°

Since H. A. is more than 180°, Az. is E.

From H. O. 214, page 82, "Declination Same Name as Latitude".

Lat. 43°, H. A. 57°, under Dec. 7° 00′ gives 28° 35.1′
  corr. for Dec. $= .72 \times 18′ = 12.96′$, or 13′

$$
\begin{aligned}
H_c \quad & 28° \; 48′ \\
H_o \quad & 28° \; 38′
\end{aligned}
$$

Intercept 10′away

Azimuth is given as 108.6° or N. 109° E.

Therefore, line of position is drawn through point 10 miles 288° from A and in direction 19°-199°, or N. 19° E. and S. 19° W.

§21. MERIDIAN ALTITUDE

One special position line must be mentioned. It is the line that you get when the sun or star is due north or south of the ship. The advantage of this line is that it depends only on the latitude of the ship and the declination of the star, and not in

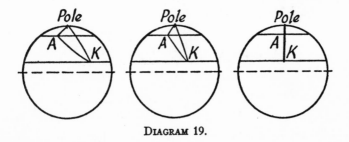

DIAGRAM 19.

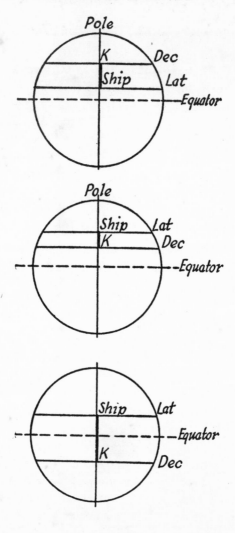

DIAGRAM 20.

any way on the G. H. A., so that it can be found without any chronometer.

The reason for this is that in the triangle K-Pole-A (Diagram 19) as K moves westward the meridian of K gradually approaches the meridian of A and the hour angle becomes smaller and smaller. As the triangle closes up the azimuth of K more nearly approaches south until finally the two meridians coincide. The hour angle becomes 0°, the azimuth is S in North Latitude, and N in South Latitude, and the *distance* from A to K is simply the difference between the latitude of A and the declination of K.

This distance from A to K (see §9) is 90° − Altitude of K, and is also called the *Zenith Distance* (Z. D.) of K. In diagram 20 it is the heavy line connecting Ship and K.

We can see that there are three ways of finding Lat. A from Dec. K (which is likewise Lat. K) and Z. D. of K.

1) Ship and K on same side of equator and Dec. K is larger than Lat. A. In this case

$$\text{Lat. A} = \text{Dec. K} - \text{Z. D.}$$

2) Ship and K on same side but Lat. A is larger than Dec. K. In this case

$$\text{Lat. A} = \text{Z. D.} + \text{Dec. K}$$

3) Ship and K on opposite sides of equator.

$$\text{Lat. A} = \text{Z. D.} - \text{Dec. K}$$

A heavenly body, as you know, attains its greatest altitude at *upper transit,* its lowest at *lower transit,* at a given place; so that, ordinarily, you would observe by sextant the increase or decrease of altitude until maximum or minimum value of the latter is reached. (*Minimum* in the case of a body above the horizon at

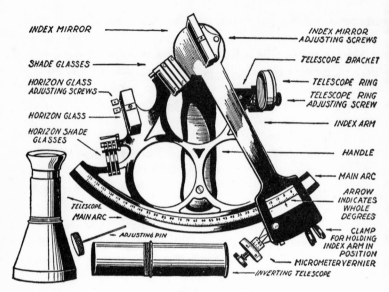

Sextant

its lower transit, or on the meridian below the elevated Pole.) Such "meridian altitude" then, *ordinarily,* would be used in finding ship's latitude, or, what amounts to the same thing, a line of position running true E. and W.

§22. Noon on Shipboard

If you do not know when it is going to be noon on board ship you will waste a lot of time standing around taking unnecessary shots so it is worth while to spend a few minutes now to see how you can tell in advance what your chronometer will read when it is noon on the ship.

The earth moves around the sun at a somewhat varying rate of speed so that the length of the solar day varies according to the time of year. But what our clocks measure is the constant average day of 24 hours. So the sun crosses the meridian sometimes earlier and sometimes later than noon, G. M. T.

Suppose we are at Greenwich and the *Nautical Almanac* tells us that on May 1, at noon, G. M. T., the sun's G. H. A. is 0° 45'. This means that the sun has already passed the meridian and is 45' of arc to the west.

15° = 1 hour, therefore
   1° = 4 minutes of time, and 45' of arc is 3/4 of 1°, or 3 minutes of time.

Therefore the sun crossed the meridian at 11h. 57m. 0s. G. M. T.

But noon comes on shipboard later than 12h. G. M. T. if you are in West longitudes, and earlier than 12h. G. M. T.

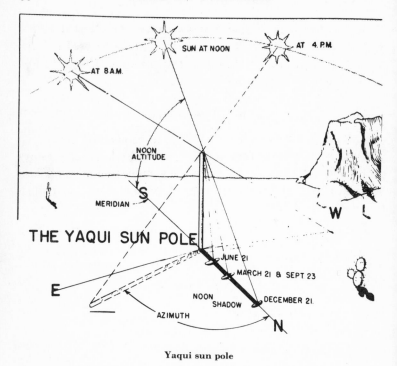

THE YAQUI SUN POLE

Yaqui sun pole

if you are in East longitudes by an amount equal to the longitude divided by 15.   If your Long. is 30 West, it will be noon on board 2 hours after that event has taken place at Greenwich.   If you are in Long. 47° 30' East, it will be noon on board 3h. 10m. before noon, G. M. T.

To take a couple of examples: On June 21 at noon, G. M. T., the sun's G. H. A. was 359° 30'.   What would your chronometer read at 1) Long. 30°W and 2) Long 30°E?

30' of arc equals 2 minutes of time.   Therefore, meridian passage takes place at 12h. 02m. 00s. G. M. T.

At Long. 30°W, meridian passage would take place at 14h. 02m. 00s. G. M. T.

At Long. 30°E, it would be 10h. 02m. 00s.

To this, of course, the chronometer error must be applied. If the clock is fast 1 minute, add one minute.   If it is slow, subtract the amount of the error.

§23. MERIDIAN PASSAGE OF STARS, MOON, PLANETS

Latitude, then, may be easily determined when the heavenly body is in transit, or bears true N. or S. of the ship, but you often will have no navigational star that is thus conveniently situated during the short period of twilight. You may, however, get the Sun's meridian altitude on any clear day at noon.

But, in higher latitudes, you have a better chance of finding your latitude when it is remembered that the body's altitude taken at *lower transit,* or meridian altitude *below* the Pole, will serve the purpose as easily as that observed on the superior meridian, or at *upper transit.* So with this second choice in the matter it will be a rare occurrence if no star is available for the kind of observation in question at either upper or lower culmination.

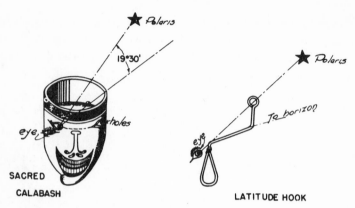

SACRED CALABASH

LATITUDE HOOK

The sacred calabash, a primitive Hawaiian navigational instrument, was a gourd through which holes were drilled, the three holes all being in one plane. The top of the gourd was leveled off at a certain distance above the holes. The gourd was filled with water until level with the holes, thus giving a horizontal surface. The top was cut down until the side opposite the hole made an angle which corresponded to the altitude of Polaris at the particular island of the user's home port. Thus, for the mainland of Hawaii, it would be 19½°. The navigator sailed for Polaris until he could just bring it over the rim of the calabash, and then followed Arcturus to the east or west until the island was reached.

The Bishop Museum in Honolulu discredits this theory of the use of the calabash, but it makes a good story anyway, and it may not be pure coincidence that the various gourds found on different islands have their tops cut off at a distance that will give Polaris an altitude which corresponds very closely to the latitude of that island. A similar instrument is in use today in the Grand Cayman Islands in the Caribbean. It consists of a wire hook which is sighted on Polaris and the horizon. It is used by the turtle fishermen of those islands and each island has its own particular hook. The turtle schooners sail far to the south of their islands in search of their prey. After the boat is loaded they sail north by compass until the proper latitude is reached, and then east until the islands are sighted.

It is also known that the South Sea Islanders used a wood frame over which strings at various angles were stretched. No one today can positively say just what particular aid these were in navigation, except that they were used in that art, and it can only be assumed that they had something to do with star azimuths. In the Solomon Islands today, the boys of the village are taught astronomy with a huge model of the sky suspended in the ceiling of the community hut. The stars are represented by various objects hung from a net overhead and the youngsters have their star lore handed down to them by word of mouth. No true Islander will hesitate to set out for a shindig on an island as much as three hundred miles distant. In their small craft with limited supplies of food and water, to miss that island means certain death, but they do not hesitate any more than people in the United States would hesitate to take a journey by air.

Time is an element that seems to be lacking in primitive navigation, but remembering the movement of the pointers of the Dipper around Polaris, it can be seen that primitive sailors had a clock which gave them fairly accurate time throughout the year. Columbus used this method of telling time in his first Atlantic voyage.

The wire latitude hook still used on the Grand Cayman Island turtle schooners is a similar instrument, each island having its own latitude hook. The fishermen sail south to hunt, return north by compass until the proper latitude is reached, then east until the islands are sighted.

Knowing that the elevation of the Pole is equal to the Latitude, the star's altitude at lower transit *plus* its polar distance (90° — Dec.) will give the desired result, or

$$\text{Lat.} = \text{Alt.} + (90° - \text{Dec.})$$

Closely connected with the observation for latitude, of course, is the chronometer time of meridian passage of body concerned. (See §22) You should, therefore, in accordance with what has been said regarding the actual sextant measurement of the meridian altitude, have at your fingers' ends the method of determining the exact time of transit of any heavenly body. This should always be Universal Time, or G. M. T., because it is never likely that ship's clock time will be correct for the longitude at observation. To repeat, you should always calculate the time your chronometer will show at transit of the star or other body; you may, of course, find the corresponding time by your clock or watch, if desired,—to the nearest minute will be close enough.

Let us now take an example of finding ship's latitude by means of the meridian altitude, both at upper and lower transits, of a star.

April 15, 1953. D. R. Lat. 35° 25′ N., Long. 47° 15′ W. At about 4:30 a.m. observed altitude of *Eltanin* on the meridian, north of ship, as 73° 58′; height of eye 40 feet. Find the latitude.

To obtain the chronometer time of star's transit: You note that the *Almanac* gives S. H. A. of *Eltanin* as 91° 06.9′, which, of course, will be S. H. A. of ship's meridian at time of transit. You also note that the longitude of your ship at instant of star's transit = the G. H. A. of star; and, since G. H. A. of star = G. H. A.♈ + S. H. A. of star, G. H. A. ♈ = Long. — S. H. A. of star. The G. M. T. corresponding to this G. H. A. ♈ value is then the G. M. T. of meridian passage of your star, as in the following:

Long.   47° 15′ W. From *Almanac:*
            360° 00′   At G. M. T. 7h. G. H. A.γ = 308° 08.6′
                            (yellow pages) 31m. 52s. =   7° 59.4′
G.H.A.* 407° 15′
S.H.A.* 91° 06.9′   At G. M. T. 7h. 31m. 52s. = 316° 08′

G.H.A.γ 316° 08′

(Note the necessary 360° increase applied to the Long.)

Therefore, your star will be on the meridian at G. M. T. 7h. 31m. 52s., and if your chronometer is, say, 8m. 10s. *slow,* the time-piece will read 7h. 23m. 42s., or 7h. 24m., which is close enough.

At this time your observed altitude is measured as 73°   58′

	corr. for ht.	— 6.0
	″ ″ refr.	— .3
	Meridian alt. 73°	51.7′
	90°	
(See § 21)	Z. D. 16°	08.3′ S.
	Dec. 51°	29.2′ N.
	Lat. 35°	21′ N.

July 30, 1953, about 2:30 a.m. D. R. Lat. 55° 05′ N., Long. 44° 50′ W. Observed altitude of *Dubhe* 27° 10′, at lower transit. Height of eye, 55 feet. Chronometer error, 7m. 12s. fast. What is the latitude?

Long.	44° 50'	W.	At G.M.T. 5h. G.H.A.γ	= 22° 32.4'
	180° 00'		(Yellow pages) 29m. 58s. =	7° 30.7'

G.H.A.* 224° 50'   At G.M.T. 5h. 29m. 58s. = 30° 03.1'
S.H.A.* 194° 46.9'

G.H.A.γ 30° 03.1'   Dec. + 62° 00.3'

Chronometer will read 5h. 37m. 10s. at star's lower transit. (Note that 180° is added to the Long. because lower transit means an increase of G. H. A. by that amount. But remember the rule still holds good that 360° must be added to G. H. A. if S. H. A. is the greater value.)

Now for the latitude: Obs. alt. *Dubhe* 27°   10'

corr for ht. eye   — 7.0'
"   "   refract.   — 1.9'

True alt. 27°   01.1'
90° — Dec., or Polar Dist. 27°   59.7'

Latitude 55°   00.8' N.

The *Nautical Almanac* gives on its daily pages the G. H. A. for Sun, Moon, and the four navigational planets, Venus, Mars, Jupiter, Saturn. Hence, a common procedure in finding G. M. T. of transit of any of these may be employed, *viz.,* that of determining the instant at which the body's G. H. A. is equal to the ship's longitude. The method is capable of a high degree of accuracy, but you are invited here to choose your preference, as you compare it with the less precise, but more popular, process of finding time of transit of Moon and planets from the table of G. M. T. of transit at the meridian of Greenwich, as given in the *Almanac*.

Example: March 17, 1959, in D. R. Lat. 30° 00' S. Long. 175° 00' E., observed altitude of *Moon's* lower limb 36° 48', bearing N.; height of eye 50 feet. What is the latitude?

Long. = *Moon's* G.H.A. = 360° − 175° E. = 185° 00'
Moon's G.H.A. at G.M.T. Mar. 17, 6h. = 182° 50.2'

$$ \overline{}$$

	2° 09.8' Diff.
From yellow pages.............	− 1.9' *v* Corr.
" " " +8m. 56s.	2° 07.9'

G.M.T. *Moon's* trans. Mar. 17, 6h. 8m. 56s.

(*Note reversal of sign in "v" correction.*)

The second method is worked as follows:

(From page 5 of *Almanac*)

Moon's transit Greenwich, March 17,	18h.	13m.
Corr. for Long. = 49m. × $\frac{175}{360}$ =		−23.8m.
Moon's transit, L.M.T., March 17,	17h.	49.2m.
Long. 175° E.	−11h.	40m.
G.M.T. of transit, March 17,	6h.	09.2m.

(Note that Local Mean Time of transit occurs *earlier* in East Long. and *later* in West Long. than same event at Greenwich.)

For the latitude:

			Obs. alt. lower		
Dec. of *Moon* at 13h.	= +22° 28.0′		limb	36°	48′
Corr. for "*v*" 83	−4.1′		(*Front cover*)		
			Dip		−6.9′
Dec. at 13h. 29m. 51s. = +22° 23.9′				36°	41.1′
			(*Back cover*) . . .		+55.6′
Moon's H.P. = 54.8′			(*Back cover*) . . .		+ 1.9′
			True alt. *Moon*	37°	38.6′
				90°	
			Z. D.	−52°	21.4′
			Dec.	+22°	23.9′
			Latitude	−29°	57.5′

Example: On the evening of same day as in preceding example, when in Long. 172° 30′ E., the meridian altitude of *Jupiter* was observed as 46° 10′, bearing N. Find G. M. T. of transit and latitude.

(*1st method*)

G. H. A. *Jupiter* = Long. = 360° − 172° 30′ E. = 187° 30′
G. H. A. *Jupiter* at G. M. T. Jan. 2, 8h.   = 182° 44.5′

(*Yellow page* xi)   19m. 02s.   4° 45.5′

G. M. T. of transit, Jan. 2,   8h. 19m. 02s.

(*The small "v" correction may be neglected in the case of planets.*)

(2nd method)

> *Jupiter's* trans. at Greenwich, Jan. 2, 19h. 47m.
>
> Corr. for Long. $= 4m. \times \dfrac{172.5}{360.0} =$ $+2m.$

> L. M. T. of transit = ...Jan. 2, 19h. 49m.
> Long. 172° 30′ = ...   −11h. 30m.

> G. M. T. of transit = ..Jan. 2,   8h. 19m.

Since the *Almanac* table indicates transit occurs 4m. *earlier* each day, the correction is *additive*. The planet crosses ship's meridian about a half day before its arrival at the Greenwich meridian; thus its local time of transit falls nearly half way between the listed times of transit at Greenwich on Jan. 1 and Jan. 2.

For the latitude:

	Obs. alt. *Jupiter*	46°	10′
	Ht. of eye	−	6.7′
	Refraction	−	0.9′
		46°	02.4′
		90°	
	Z. D.	−43°	57.6′
(From Almanac, Jan. 2, 8.3h)	Dec.	+14°	04.3′
	Lat.	−29°	53.3′

To find the expected altitude of a star at its transit, from the D. R. Latitude subtract star's declination, *algebraically;* the result is star's zenith distance. Then 90° − Z. D. = Meridian Alt.

Example: Find the approximate sextant altitude of *Capella*, which star culminates at about 18h. 37m. on March 1, 1953, in Lat. 10° 20′ N., Long. 30° W. Height of observer's eye is 60 feet.

D. R. Latitude	+10°	20′	(The resulting sign given
Dec. *Capella*	+45°	57′	the Z. D., which in this
			case is — or S., indicates
Z. D.	−35°	37′	observer will face N. in
	90°		observing the star.)
	54°	23′	
Ht. of eye	+ 7′		(sign reversed)
Sextant to be set	54°	30′	

With this reading set on your sextant, sweep the northern horizon a little to and fro and you will be surprised to note how easily the star is picked up, even with your altitude considerably wide of the truth.

Although not exactly within the pale of the meridian passage problem, you have in the star *Polaris,* which lies less than a degree from the North celestial pole, a special convenient means of obtaining an E-W line of position while in northern latitudes. In azimuth the star's greatest departure from true N. ranges from only 1°, in Lats. 0° to 25°, to less than 3° in Lat. 70°. Complete data for finding both latitude and azimuth are given on pages 274-276 of the *Almanac.*

Example: On the evening of March 1, 1969, in D. R. Lat. 30° 00′ N., Long. 135° 15′ W., observed altitude of *Polaris* is 30° 40′.

Height of eye 50 feet. G. M. T. of observation, March 2, 3h. 40m.
Find the latitude and star's azimuth.

G.H.A.γ, Mar. 2, 3h. = 204° 36.6′ Obs. alt.
for 40m. = + 10° 01.6′

G.H.A.γ, Mar. 2, at 3h.
40m. = 214° 38.2′
Long. W. = 135° 15′

L.H.A.γ = 79° 23.2′

Polaris alt.	30°	40′
Dip (*50 feet*)		− 6.9′
Refraction		− 1.6′
Polaris Tables, p. 274,		+24.6′
,, ,, ,,		+ .5′
,, ,, ,,		+ .8′
	30°	57.4′
Constant	− 1°	00′
Latitude	+29°	57.4′

The line of position is the latitude line at N 29° 57.4′

Azimuth, page 274, = −0.8°, = N. 1° W.

Chapter V

§24. Identifying the Stars

The easiest way to identify the stars is to learn what they look like and how they are related to other stars. For instance, of the twenty-odd stars most used in navigation, nine are closely related to the constellation Orion. Betelgeuse and Rigel, two very bright stars, are at diagonally opposite corners of the parallelogram surrounding the three stars of the Belt of Orion.

The stars of the Belt point to Sirius, the brightest star in the sky. (See Diagram 21.) Sirius, Betelgeuse, and Procyon form a nearly equilateral triangle. Aldebaran is about as far from the Belt as Sirius is, but in the opposite direction, and so on. However if the sky is partly cloudy it may be impossible to recognize the stars by sight. It is then necessary to identify them from the tables.

Any star can be identified if we know its altitude and azimuth. So, if you are not sure which star you have observed, take a compass bearing of it as soon as you have the altitude. *This bearing must be corrected for variation and deviation in order to get the true azimuth before you start looking up the star.*

The altitude of the star gives its distance from the ship, the azimuth is its bearing, and we know the dead reckoning latitude of the ship. Therefore we have two sides Pole-A and A-K and one angle Pole-A-K of the navigation triangle (see Diagram 12, page 25) and can solve for latitude of K and hour angle between ship and K, using the *Navigation Tables* according to directions for identifying stars. (We do not need to know either the lati-

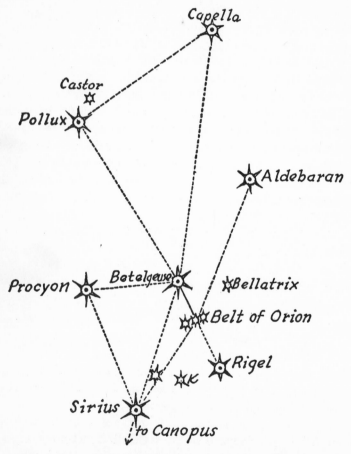

DIAGRAM 21. BETELGEUSE-PROCYON-SIRIUS AND BETELGEUSE-POLLUX-CAPELLA FORM EQUILATERAL TRIANGLES. SIRIUS IS THE BRIGHTEST, CANOPUS THE SECOND BRIGHTEST STAR.

tude of the ship or bearing of the star with any extreme accuracy, as the stars that are bright enough to be useful in navigation are widely spaced throughout the sky, and there is little possibility of confusion).

If we know the declination and sidereal hour angle of a star we can find its name in the *Nautical Almanac*.

We get declination directly from the *Navigation Tables*.

The G. H. A. of the star is obtained by combining the longitude of the ship and the hour angle contained in the *Tables*, in the following way: If the star's bearing is west, call the hour angle +. If the bearing is east, call the hour angle —, then take the algebraic sum of hour angle and longitude, calling west longitudes + and east longitudes —. In other words, add if the signs are alike and subtract the smaller from the larger if the signs are not alike. For example:

$$
\begin{array}{lll}
\text{Long. ship} & 60\ \text{E} = & -60° \\
\text{H. A.} & 90\ \text{W} = & \underline{\quad 90°} \\
\text{G. H. A.} & & 30° \ \text{(G. H. A. is always West} \\
& & \text{from Greenwich)}
\end{array}
$$

$$
\begin{array}{lll}
\text{Long. ship} & 60\ \text{W} = & 60° \\
\text{H. A.} & 90\ \text{W} = & \underline{\quad 90°} \\
\text{G. H. A.} & & 150°
\end{array}
\qquad
\begin{array}{lll}
\text{Long. ship} & 60\ \text{E} = & -60° \\
\text{H. A.} & 90\ \text{E} = & \underline{-90°} \\
& & -150°
\end{array}
$$

In this last case we must subtract 150° from 360° to get the G. H. A., since G. H. A. is always a west longitude. Therefore G. H. A. is 210°.

$$
\begin{array}{lll}
\text{Long. ship} & 60\ \text{W} = & 60° \\
\text{H. A.} & 90\ \text{E} = & \underline{-90°} \\
\text{G. H. A.} & & -30°
\end{array}
$$

Subtract 30° from 360° to get G. H. A. = 330°

To state the above briefly, by following the directions in the tables we find declination and hour angle of our star. If the bearing of the star from the ship is west, call the H. A. +, and if the bearing is east, call H. A. −. We combine this with the dead reckoning longitude of the ship, calling W. Long. + and E. Long. − and get the G. H. A. of the star at the time of observation. If the result is −, subtract it from 360°.

Since the G. H. A. thus found is equal to G. H. A. of γ (corrected for minutes and seconds of G. M. T.) + the star's S. H. A. (sidereal hour angle), then to obtain star's S. H. A. we subtract G. H. A. of γ from G. H. A. of star, increasing the last-named by 360°, if necessary, or,

S. H. A. of star = G. H. A. of star − G. H. A. of γ.

Then we look in either the column headed STARS in the daily pages or in the list of stars given on pages 268 to 273 of the *Almanac* and select the star whose S. H. A. and Declination agree closest with the values obtained by means of the tables.

(It is usually quite easy to tell a star from a planet, because the stars twinkle and planets do not. However, this is not always true. If the S. H. A. and Declination do not fit any *star,* then look in the hourly positions of the *planets* given for each day in *Almanac. Venus* and *Jupiter* are brighter than any star and *Mars* is distinctly reddish. *Saturn* is a pale yellow. These are the only planets you are likely to observe.)

Example: On the evening of March 4, 1953, an unknown star is observed. Greenwich time of observation 23h. 30h.; altitude 63° 46′; azimuth N. 18° E.; D. R. Lat. (to nearest whole degree) 42° S.; D. R. Long. (to nearest whole degree) 62° W.

Follow directions in the table and find the star's Dec. as 17° S. and H. A. 8°. This is 8° E., as the azimuth is East. Therefore G. H. A. is 62° − 8° = 54°.

From this G. H. A. of 54°, increased by a whole circle, as required in this instance, or 414°, we subtract the G. H. A. of γ (corrected for time of observation) which amounts to 154° 55' or roughly 155°. We now have 414° — 155°, or 259°, as approximate S. H. A. of star.

A glance down the S. H. A. column on page 254 of the *Almanac* shows that 259° closely approaches the value given for *Sirius*, and the Declination indicated, — 16° 39', falls near to our 17° S. taken from the tables. Our star, therefore, is *Sirius*.

With the aid of the Star Chart included in the *Nautical Almanac* you should have little difficulty in recognizing any navigational star on a clear night; so that, with some practice in its use, the memory may be relied upon to identify the various groups in partly cloudy sky conditions.

The *Almanac* now includes maps of both the Northern and the Southern heavens and also of the complete equatorial belt between 30° N. and 30° S. This present arrangement simplifies the matters of star identification and plotting the given position of a planet, relative places of the various star groups, with the *S.H.A.* and *Declination* data, being more clearly "lined up" in the heavenly dome than was possible from the former mercatorial map.

If you have figured up the S. H. A. of your meridian for your local time of scanning the heavens, as, let us say, 10 p.m., April 7, 1953, while in Lat. 40° N. and Long. 60° W., your work will be like this:

Local time, April 7,	22h.	Long. = G.H.A. =	60°
Long. 60° W.	+ 4h.		+360°
Greenwich time,	=26h.		420°
	—24h.	G.H.A.γ at 2h. =	226°
or April 8,	2h.	Your S.H.A. =	194°

This means that your meridian, represented by a vertical line, measures 194° along the celestial equator (horizontal line marked 0°) from the vernal equinox, or γ, at extreme left of chart at 0°, which is the same point at extreme right, if the map's ends were made to meet and thus present the natural circular shape of the equator or zero-declination line.

For proper basic conception of the starry situation it is most important to note that, while the S. H. A. of each star has a fixed value (neglecting its usually small annual change), the G. H. A. of the vernal equinox, or γ, is *increasing* at the rate of 15° 02.5′ per hour and your S. H. A., which is the hour angle of your meridian from γ, or L. H. A. γ, is *decreasing* at same rate. (This may be checked by taking 11 p.m. as your local time of observation. You then have an increase of G. H. A. γ by 15°, which leaves your S. H. A. as 179°, instead of 194°.)

So with the march of time your meridian may be conceived as sweeping the star map from West to East at the Earth's speed of rotation, or through 360° in one day.

In the present example, your S. H. A. (hour angle of your meridian from γ) is 194°. If the star chart is held overhead as indicated, you will observe just N. of your zenith the two stars forming the West side of the bowl of the "Big Dipper".

Note that *Dubhe* and its mate, *Merak*, about 6° to the southward, give you a pointing line northward toward *Polaris,* the "Pole Star", at a distance from *Dubhe* of about 29°, or about the length of the "Big Dipper" itself. These two are known as the "Pointers" on that account, and by their means you will never be at a loss to recognize *Polaris* throughout the varying positions the group assumes in its apparent revolution about that star throughout each 24-hour day. *Dubhe* would be at upper transit at 3 minutes before 10 o'clock, as his S. H. A. is given as 194° 46′.

About 28° southward and a little West of your zenith the bright *Regulus,* principal member in Leo, is recognized. S. H. A. of that star being 208° 31', its L. H. A. is 14½° at 10 p.m., so that you note it crossed your meridian 58 minutes before that hour, since 4° = 1 minute of time. *Regulus* lies at the southern extremity, you notice, of a group forming a fair semblance of a sickle which extends about 15° northward. A short distance East of the "Sickle" is a well-defined right-angled triangle, with *Denebola* marking its eastern corner.

If you follow the curve of the Big Dipper's handle, at about 30° from *Alkaid* at tail end of the handle, you will meet bright *Arcturus,* which should now bear about S.E. Continue the curve for another 30° and you meet *Spica.* S.W. of *Spica* you should easily discern the outline of the "Cutter's Mainsail", the gaff of which points directly toward, and at about 12° from *Spica.*

Orion should be low in the West and you will note that a line from *Regulus* to "Orion's Belt" (3 stars close together in a N.E.-S.W. line) passes close to *Procyon* at a little more than half way to the *Orion* group. The middle star in "Orion's Belt", by the way, is called *Alnilam.*

Following the chart in a similar manner, you may become acquainted with as many stars as you wish, if you observe from night to night the gradual appearing of new constellations. (The stars rise earlier each night by 3m. 55.91s. of clock time, due to the apparent eastward travel of the Sun in the ecliptic.) In less than a year you will have covered the heavens, even if remaining in Lat. 40° N., to the limit of about the parallel of declination 45° S.

At the time and date of our study, you would observe the group *Cassiopeia,* or the "Lady's Chair", *below* the Pole. It has the form of an irregular W. *Schedar* and *Caph,* its brightest members, form one of the outer legs, *Schedar* occupying the southernmost angle. It is worthy of mention that when either the small star at the other end of this constellation (listed as ε *Cassiopeiae*) or *Alkaid* at the tail end of the *Great Bear* ("Big Dipper") is vertically *above* or vertically *below Polaris,* all three are practically on the meridian and bear true North. (*Polaris* now is within one degree of the Pole.)

Chapter VI

§25. Aerial Navigation

Navigation from airplanes is no different in theory from navigation at sea. The only difference in the use of the Tables is that if you use an artificial horizon (bubble sextant) instead of the real horizon there is no correction for height of eye. Also, the correction for refraction, etc., is different and must be taken from the table "Bubble Sextant" in the *Navigation Tables*.

Owing to the great speed of planes it is essential to get the position quickly if it is to be of any use. However, it is not necessary to know your position as exactly as if you were on board ship. An *Air Almanac* has been compiled, which is a simplified form of the *Nautical Almanac*. Simplified tables for use in working out the navigation triangle have also been published. These speed up the work so that a position can be worked out in about 5 minutes after taking the observations.

It is frequently much more difficult to get accurate altitudes from a plane than from a ship because of the bumpy motion of a plane. For this reason it is the common practice to take a series of observations of the same star, five or more, as quickly as possible, and average the readings and the times.

If the observations of the two stars needed for the intersecting position lines are not taken quickly, it will be necessary to advance the position line of the first star in the same manner as when navigating by the sun.

Because of the probable inaccuracy of the observations, it is even more important to get a good cut in air navigation than at sea. (See §26, Notes on What Star to Shoot, pages 82–3, and Diagram 17, page 52)

An interesting development in Air Navigation is the publication of *H. O. 249* which contains the calculated azimuths and altitudes of stars, sun, moon, and planets in three volumes. Volume I of these "Sight Reduction Tables" gives the computed altitudes and azimuths of 34 selected stars, 19 of which are of the first magnitude and 15 of the second, corresponding to each even-numbered degree of Local Hour Angle of γ in Latitudes 70° to 89° and every degree in Latitudes 0° to 69°.

The tables are so arranged that the altitudes and azimuths of seven different stars are shown in the same line, so that, with a given Local Hour Angle of γ, two or more of the group may be chosen according to their location in azimuth, where a satisfactory "cut" of the resulting lines of position is desired.

Computed for a certain epoch, the tabular values given are for the given epoch in Volume I and must be corrected for other years in the period following, on account of changes in astronomical measurements caused by the phenomena of precession and nutation. This is taken care of in an auxiliary table included in the volume. Volume I is reprinted every few years so that the corrections will never be too large.

Since the *Sight Reduction Tables* are equally adaptable to surface navigation, let us use Volume I and find what other bright stars are in suitable position for observation at time of taking the altitude of *Procyon* in the example shown in §19.

G. M. T. is January 1, 10h. 8m. 0s.; D. R. Lat. 43° 12′ N., Long. 60° 15′ W. From either the *Nautical* or the *Air Almanac* we get:

G. H. A. γ at 10h. 8m. = 250° 48′

Longitude, assumed = 60° 48′ W. Assumed Lat.=43° N.

L. H. A. γ = 190° 00′

In Volume I (epoch 1970.0), on page headed LAT 43° N. and abreast of L. H. A. γ 190° we find the following calculated altitudes (H_c) and azimuths (Z_n) of stars indicated thus:

	Kochab	Vega	Arcturus	Spica	Regulus	Pollux	Capella
H_c	55° 25′	25° 55′	59° 08′	35° 05′	44° 46′	29° 51′	17° 46′
Z_n	015°	060°	133°	167°	239°	282°	317°

So you see that resulting position lines from *Arcturus, Regulus,* and *Capella* as a group, or from *Vega, Spica,* and *Pollux,* will present an admirable "cut" in both instances, by simply noting the differences in azimuths of the stars. (See §26)

It also will be noted that *H. O. 249* serves as a star identification table second to none, in that seven navigational stars are pointed out to us at a glance, with only the Latitude and Local Hour Angle of γ to consider.

Chapter VII

§26. Notes on What Star to Shoot

The *Nautical Almanac* lists the declination and the S. H. A. of 57 bright stars. On a clear night as many as twenty of these may be above the horizon at one time, so you have a wide choice.

There are two important things to take into consideration: accuracy of the observation and accuracy of the intersection. The accuracy of the observation depends first on your skill with the sextant, and second, on atmospheric conditions. For a beginner, the brighter the star the easier it is to pick out and to bring down to the horizon, so you should choose a good, bright star. You will, anyway, so it is hardly worth mentioning.

Of the bright stars in sight you must take one whose altitude is not less than 10 degrees (15 degrees is better), because if a star is lower there will probably be an abnormal refraction of some kind and the star may be lower or higher than your observation indicates.

Next you should look at the horizon under your star, and the sea under the horizon. Haze is bad, and also low lying bands of horizontal clouds, or dark and light streaks in the water. Any of these make the true horizon difficult to see distinctly especially when it is observed through the sextant.

The accuracy of the intersection depends on two things: the

altitude of each star and the relative positions of the two stars whose position lines you are going to plot.

The altitude of the star should not be too high because the whole plan of intersecting position lines is based on the fact that K is so far from the ship that an arc of a position circle is practically a straight line. Now if K is near the ship (which is the same as saying that the altitude of the star is high), a 30-mile arc of the position circle will differ appreciably from a straight line. So do not choose a star whose altitude is greater than 65 degrees.

Lastly, the nearer the angle of intersection is to 90 degrees the better, so choose two stars whose bearings are not closer than 30 degrees to each other.

To summarize: choose a bright star with an altitude between 15 and 65 degrees, which is over a clear and distinct patch of horizon, and a similar star whose bearing makes an angle of not less than 30 degrees with the bearing of the first star.

You will find that these considerations limit your choice considerably and sometimes it will be impossible to fulfill even one of these requirements. Then you will have to fall back on the law of averages, shooting four or five different stars and plotting the position line for each star. The result will be a little network of intersecting lines. (See Diagram 22.) and you pick out *the point which comes closest to all the lines* as the probable position of your ship. The most probable position is that marked in the diagram, and the error should not be greater than the radius of the little circle.

§27. NOTE ON COMMON MISTAKES

I write this note from the heart as I have made all the mistakes mentioned in it not once, but many times.

The most annoying thing that you can do when taking the altitudes of several stars is to be in such a hurry that you forget to record your sextant reading. You take an altitude, rush to the chronometer, read it, write down the time, and hurry out

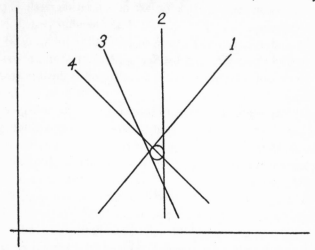

DIAGRAM 22.

again without looking at the sextant to shoot another star. To forget to record your reading is such a stupid thing that it seems impossible that anyone could make such an error; but wait until you try it yourself some evening when a big bank of clouds is moving across the sky and blotting out all your stars.

When you convert your observed altitude to true altitude you must not forget that the correction is different according to whether you have observed a star or the sun. For a star the correction is subtracted, while for the sun it is added. The correction differs in amount as well as in sign and the tables are clearly marked at the top "sun's corr." and "star's corr." with a + and a − sign. So there is no excuse for making a mistake. Nevertheless it has been done.

It is not only possible, but probable, that you will occasionally call your azimuth N W when it should be N E, or if you get it right in your workbook, that you will lay it off on your chart N W just the same.

And when it comes to looking up figures in the tables (except in H. O. 214), the opportunities for getting into trouble are, what might be called, legion. It is so easy to get in the wrong column, and even if you don't, there is no difficulty at all in transposing figures while copying them out.

There is also the opportunity to add or subtract incorrectly and to forget in the heat of the moment that there are 60 minutes to a degree instead of 100. So that, for example, when you perform the following:

$$32° \ 08'$$
$$-14° \ 57'$$

you will write the answer 17° 51′ instead of 17° 11′.

So don't get into the habit, when your position lines intersect in what seems a peculiar position, of saying, "There must be strong currents around here," instead, check all your figures starting from the very beginning and you will probably find that the mistake was there after all. When you are absolutely certain that your observations and figuring are correct then it will be time to begin talking about currents.

There is no way to be sure that you haven't made a mistake in your observations because you can't go back and check the chronometer, and the sextant has been reset for all but the last altitude. So if the position is of any importance you should take three altitudes of each star, noting the time at each altitude, and plot all three position lines. This does not require much more work, for the mean of all three altitudes and chronometer times usually will be nearer the truth than a single observation; or, if it is not possible to take three sights in smart succession, the position line and intercept for your first altitude may be plotted, subsequent changes of altitude allowed for (according to differences in time and rate of altitude change) and so compared with the result of first observation. If your sights are consistent and the first one correctly computed and plotted, all three lines of position will coincide.

An error in the dead reckoning longitude will cause you to select the wrong longitude for A, and therefore for your hour angle. If your calculated altitude is more than 30' from the true altitude try an hour angle 1 degree greater than the one you have used and see if that fixes things. If not, try an hour angle 1 degree less than the first one. If that doesn't mend matters either, check your figures again. After this you have your choice of excuses.

You may have made a mistake in identifying your star. The horizon may have been deceptive. If you have been shooting the sun in very hot weather there is always the possibility of abnormal refraction. But whatever may be the cause, if the error is in your observations, that sight and its position line must be thrown out.

If you have observations of only two stars and one of them must be thrown out you haven't any intersection. For this reason it is advisable to take three sights each of at least three different stars, and four stars are better than three. This is especially good advice in rough weather when a distant wave top may appear like the true horizon. Then out of nine or twelve position lines you will get a pretty fair idea of your probable position. (See Diagram 23.)

Star 1 is not to be trusted. The center line for Star 2 is probably not far from the true position line. Star 3 has two points on the same line, so regard that line as the true position line. Take the blacked-in circle as more or less your position, with an area

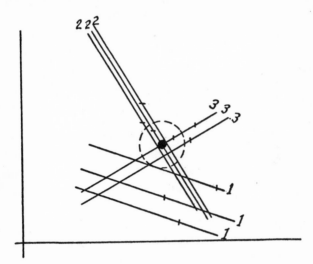

DIAGRAM 23.

of doubt extending as far as the dotted circle. Conditions would have to be pretty bad for you to get such bad intersections, but sometimes conditions *are* pretty bad, and then you have to do the best you can.

Navigation isn't an exact science. Questions of judgment enter into it. So don't put science ahead of common sense. Even though you have plotted a good position, if it seems completely unreasonable to you don't trust blindly in your figures. There are such things as compensating errors.

The only thing to do, as was once said to me, is "Always remember that you might not be where you think you are."

If *either* your figures or your common sense show that you are getting into danger, you must play safe, assume that you are in the more dangerous position, and get out of it as soon as you can. You may feel foolish, and you may lose a little time, but if you wreck your ship you will feel worse than foolish and possibly lose more than time.

However, proficiency in taking and working out sextant observations can be attained only by practice, practice,—and *more* practice. You may be pleasantly surprised at results achieved.

Chapter VIII

§28. DEFINITIONS

ALTITUDE is the elevation, as measured in degrees, etc., of arc, of a heavenly body's center above the horizon. The observed altitude, usually indicated by H_s, is that actually measured by the sextant. This, when corrected for height of eye and refraction, gives the *true altitude*, H_o, in the case of a star, further corrected for parallax in the case of observed altitudes of planets *Venus* and *Mars,* and, in that of the *Sun* and *Moon,* for semi-diameter and parallax. When observing an altitude of the Sun, the *lower limb,* or lowest point of the disk, is brought in contact with the horizon in the sextant. That of the Moon's illuminated limb is taken, and this may be her *upper* or *lower* limb.

ASSUMED POSITION is a point near the dead reckoning position. Its latitude is the full degree nearest the dead reckoning latitude. Its longitude is such that it differs from the longitude of K, which also is the Greenwich hour angle of K, by a number of whole degrees.

AZIMUTH is the bearing of a heavenly object from an observer. The *Tables* give *true* bearing and not *compass* bearing. Don't forget this when plotting position lines. Usually symbolized by Z, it may be expressed as a number of degrees from true North, or 0°, through 360°; from true N. or from true S. toward E. or W. through 180°; or up to 90° only, from N. or from S. toward E.

or W. Thus an azimuth of 275°, S.95°W., or N.85°W. indicate the same bearing. The first-named value usually is distinguished as Z_n 275°. (Azimuth is analogous to the *great circle* course toward a distant point on the earth's surface in that, with the difference of longitude and latitude of destination respectively substituting *hour angle* and *declination* in the *Tables*, the value given is the true *initial* course for following the great circle track.)

BEARING is the angle between a line connecting two points and the meridian, or N.-S. line.

CALCULATED ALTITUDE is that which would have been observed if ship were at the assumed position at time of observation.

COMPASS ROSE is the circle marked off in degrees, which you will find in the corner of the charts. It is marked from 0° in a clockwise direction all the way around the circle to 360°. It has an arrow pointing to true north. Inside the circle there is usually a smaller concentric circle showing magnetic directions. The north arrow of this circle is at an angle to the true north arrow, at an amount and direction corresponding to the variation of the compass for the region covered by the chart. This magnetic circle is useful in laying off compass courses, but should never be used in plotting position lines as all calculated azimuths are measured from true north.

DEAD RECKONING is your best guess as to the ship's position. It is based on your opinion as to how far and in what direction you have come since the last position you were certain of.

DECLINATION is the latitude of K. North declinations are marked N and south declinations S.

DEGREES are expressed either as degrees of angle or degrees of arc. Two radii at an angle of, say, 10 degrees will mark off an arc of 10 degrees on the circumference of the circle. The length

of an arc is proportional to the length of the radius. (See LATI-
TUDE and LONGITUDE.)

DRAWING INSTRUMENTS. Parallel rulers, dividers, pencil and
eraser (and particularly the eraser), are all the drawing instruments needed. The man who sells you the parallel rule will show
you how to use it.

GREENWICH MEAN TIME is the time which a clock at Greenwich
would read at the moment that you take your observations.
Your corrected chronometer reading gives you G. M. T.

HOUR ANGLE is the angle at the Pole between the respective
hour circles or meridians passing through two points, or it may
be defined as the arc of the equinoctial, or celestial equator, intercepted by the hour circles or meridians passing respectively
through two given points, measured westward. Local hour angle
(L. H. A.), which may be expressed E. or W., is the angle at
the Pole formed by an observer's meridian and the hour circle or
meridian passing through a heavenly body or through some specified point in the heavens. Analogous to *difference of longitude,* the
Greenwich hour angle (G. H. A.) of a body at upper transit is
equal to that measurement, always considered in a westerly direction; thus, an observer's meridian or a body in transit at such
meridian, as in Long. 160° E., has a G. H. A. of 360° − 160° E.
= 200°. Hour angle may be expressed in either arc or time
measure; 15° = 1 hour, 15′ = 1 minute, and 15″ = 1 second of
time; 1° = 4 minutes, 1′ = 4 seconds, and 1″ = .067 second of
time.

INTERCEPT is the difference in miles (minutes of arc) between
the calculated altitude (H_c) and the corrected observed, or true,
altitude (H_o) : or, the distance from assumed position (A) either
in the direction of the azimuth *toward* or in the opposite direction

away from it, at which the position line is plotted at right angles to the azimuth. When H_o is greater than H_c, the intercept is distinguished as *toward,* as opposed to *away* when H_o is less than H_c.

K is the projection of a star on the earth's surface, the point at which a straight line drawn from the center of the star to the center of the earth would cut the earth's surface. The latitude and longitude of this point for any moment of Greenwich civil time can be found from the data given in the *Nautical Almanac.*

LATITUDE is measured in degrees from the equator to the poles. Lat. Equator $= 0°$, Lat. North Pole $= 90°$ N, Lat. South Pole $= 90°$ S. One minute of latitude is always equal to 1 mile. When taking distances to scale off your chart always set your dividers along the scale at the side of the chart, and *never*, unless you are at the equator, set them along the top or the bottom scale.

LONGITUDE is measured east and west from the meridian of Greenwich, which is $0°$, to the International date line, which is $180°$, and is the place where east and west do meet. One minute of longitude is 1 mile at the *equator*, and nothing at the poles. You must never forget this and take off distances from the *longitude* scale at the top and the bottom of the chart. In certain problems it is more convenient to convert an *East* longitude into a *West* one by subtracting it from $360°$, as, for example, before deducting the G. H. A. in determining the S. H. A. of an observer's meridian.

MERIDIAN ALTITUDE is observed when the heavenly body is "in transit", or at instant of crossing observer's meridian, at which time the body bears N. or S. true. Unless otherwise specified, it is that occurring at *upper transit,* when the body's greatest altitude is attained on the day in question. The meridian altitude *below* the Pole, or that occurring at *lower transit,* is the converse of this.

POSITION CIRCLE is a hypothetical circle drawn with its center at K, with a radius equal to 5400' — altitude, when altitude is expressed in minutes of arc. The ship is somewhere on this circle.

POSITION LINE is a straight line equivalent to a small arc of the position circle. The ship is somewhere on this line.

SEXTANT is an instrument used to measure angles. There is no use in trying to describe one in words or even with diagrams. It is much easier and quicker to understand how to work one when you can actually hold it in your hand and have someone explain its use to you. The explanation can wait until you are ready to buy one, when you can have it demonstrated in any nautical instrument shop.

SIDEREAL HOUR ANGLE is the *westerly* hour angle of a celestial body from the vernal equinox. With its brother co-ordinate, the declination, it is given for each star listed in the *Nautical Almanac* and thus locates the point in the heavens occupied by a particular star. When the star is on the observer's meridian above the Pole (upper transit), the sidereal hour angle of both star and meridian have identical values. It is abbreviated as S. H. A.

TRANSIT is the meridian passage of a heavenly body. Lower transit is that over the meridian *below* the elevated Pole.

VERNAL EQUINOX is the zero-point from which the sidereal hour angle of a star is measured. Also called First Point of Aries and usually symbolized by γ, its G. H. A. for each hour of Greenwich Mean Time (G. M. T.) is given in the daily pages of our *Nautical Almanac.*

ZENITH is the point in the sky directly over the observer. A line drawn from the observer to the zenith is perpendicular to the plane of the horizon.

ZENITH DISTANCE is 90° — Altitude.

Chapter IX

§29. OTHER NAVIGATION TABLES

H. O. 208 (Dreisonstok) and H. O. 211 (Ageton) were, until H. O. 214 was published, the standard navigation tables. Each has its advantages and disadvantages. Dreisonstok uses a slightly shorter method, but Ageton leaves the reader less confused about azimuths. Both give satisfactory results.

Both Dreisonstok and Ageton give all latitudes up to 90°. No mathematics other than simple addition and subtraction are called for in either book.

But, when using either book, the most careful attention must be paid to every step of the process and the directions must be strictly followed. If the rules say to look in column A you must not look in column B. If the rules say to subtract Z' from Z'', you must not add the two quantities. And even though 22162 looks very much like 22612, and 31578 like 35178, you will get into considerable trouble if you overlook the difference.

So read the directions carefully, follow them exactly, and copy the figures into your workbook without transposing even one of them. If you can do all this every time you will have no difficulty in using the tables.

§30. HOW TO USE DREISONSTOK

On page 1 there are two sets of tables for sextant corrections, Table B for height of eye above sea-level, and Table A for the lump-sum correction of refraction, etc. These require no explanation. But you can save time and maybe avoid some errors if you add the index error of your sextant to the correction for height of eye and add the sum to the corrections in Table A.

For example: Let us say that when you are on deck taking an altitude the height of your eye above the water is 10 feet (correction $+2'.7$, in Table B) and the index error of your sextant is $+2'$. The sum of these corrections is $+4'.7$ which we call $+5'$. Now add $5'$ to every figure in the right-hand column of Table A and write the result in *pencil* to the right of the table. (I specify pencil because the index error changes from time to time and must be checked at intervals.)

For observed altitude $22°$ the star's correction in Table A is $-8'.2$ and if you add $5'$ to this you get $-3'$ to write at the side. Now you have all your corrections for altitude combined into one figure, and if your sextant altitude is $22° 14'$ you see at a glance that the true altitude is $22° 11'$.

Table III is of no interest to us.

Tables I and II are what we use to find the calculated altitude and are followed by an explanation of the construction and use of the tables. Nothing that I have said will have prepared you to understand a word of the first two pages of this, so you can skip that part of the detailed explanation. The first three parts of the explanation are out of date now because the latest *Almanac* gives G. H. A. at sight.

We can start with the hour angle as calculated in the way that I have already explained. Dreisonstok calls this hour angle t in Table I, and *local hour angle* or L. H. A. when talking about it. In either case it means what we have been calling hour angle.

Notes 5, 7, 9, 10, 12, and 14, I think, require a little further explanation.

Note 5.—You must remember that in the *Almanac*, north declinations are + and south declinations are −. Latitudes are also referred to as + and −. The "signs" mentioned in line 2 of Note 5 are the signs of the declination and the latitude. If both are + or both are −, you *add* the declination to *b* in Table I. If one is + and one is −, you take the *difference* between the declination and *b*.

Note 7—H_c is what we have called the calculated altitude; H_o is used for the true altitude.

Note 9.—The "elevated pole" is the North Pole if the ship is in north latitudes and the South Pole if the ship is in south latitudes.

The azimuth (obtained by adding Z' and Z'' from the tables) will always be a number between 0° and 180°, and the N. E. S. and W., are added according to rule: N when the ship is in N. Lat., S when the ship is in S. Lat., and E or W according to whether K is east or west of the ship. (See §16.)

Note 10.—This says only that the hour angle is always measured to the west around the whole 360 degrees.

Notes 12 and 14.—If you are willing to take things as they come and wait until a situation arises before you worry about it, you can skip the following paragraphs of this section.

But if reading Notes 12 and 14 gives you a slightly dizzy feeling you should read on.

Note 12 says that "if the hour angle is between 90° and 270° the azimuth is obtained by subtraction." And Note 14 says that if $d + b$ is more than 90° give "the resultant Z''" a negative sign." Naturally one wonders what to do if the hour angle is 105° and $d + b$ should turn out to be 98°. What about the subtractions and the negative signs then? Well, the simplest way to handle this situation is to state at once that *if* the hour angle is between

90° and 270° it is impossible for $d + b$ to be more than 90°. You will never have to apply both rules at once.

This fact can be explained most simply by taking a concrete example. Say that a star is visible when its hour angle is 105°. 105° is equal to 7 hours, so the star would be above the horizon at least 14 out of the 24 hours. But a star is never above the horizon for more than 12 hours unless both star and observer are in the same hemisphere, and in this case latitude and declination are both north or both south.

Rule 12 says that if H. A. is more than 90°, we give b the opposite sign to the latitude, therefore we must subtract b from the declination and $d - b$ (or $b - d$) must be less than 90°, because neither b nor d can be greater than 90°.

So if hour angle is between 90° and 270°, $d + b$ is always less than 90°, and if $d + b$ is greater than 90° the hour angle (or its explement) cannot be between 90° and 270°. Therefore you never have to apply both Note 12 and Note 14 to the same problem.

§31. How to Use Ageton

Ageton differs from H. O. 214 and Dreisonstok in that he uses the dead reckoning position instead of an assumed position. For this reason it is necessary to go through more steps in solving the navigation triangle K-Pole-A. However there is only one table instead of two as in Dreisonstok, and also you get the azimuth directly instead of by adding Z' and Z'', so that there is one less opportunity to go wrong.

The tables are made up of a series of double columns, headed by degrees and half degrees, from 0° to 90°, with the intermediate minutes set down the sides. The left-hand column of each of the double columns is marked A and the right-hand column, B.

In the formulas to be given, the subscripts A and B show which column is to be used. For instance:

Dec. A means that you take your declination (to the nearest minute) and copy the number in the left-hand side of the double column; Dec. B means that the number in the right-hand side is to be copied.

Since dead reckoning position is used, the hour angle and latitude, as well as the declination, may have odd minutes. The formula is as follows:

$$\text{H. A.}_A + \text{Dec.}_B = R_A$$

Find R in the A column and copy the corresponding figure in the B column. This is called R_B.

$R_B - \text{Dec.}_A = k_A$ (This "k" has no relation to the K we have been using to designate the known point.)

Next look up k_A in the A column and find the degrees and minutes corresponding to it. This is called k and has the same sign, north or south, as the declination of your star.

From this k, you subtract the latitude of your dead reckoning if latitude and k are of the same sign. If one is north and one is south, you add instead of subtract.

You find the B of this (k-Lat.) and add to it the number R_B that you have already found. This sum is the A of the altitude. You look up the sum in the A column, and the corresponding angle is the altitude.

You take the B of the altitude and subtract from it the R_A, that you have already found. The remainder is the A of your azimuth. You look it up in the A column, and the corresponding angle is the azimuth.

This can be more conveniently written as follows:

$$\text{H. A.}_A + \text{Dec.}_B = R_A$$
$$R_B - \text{Dec.}_A = k_A \quad \text{(give k the same sign as Dec.)}$$
$$(k - \text{Lat.})_B + R_B = \text{Alt.}_A$$
$$\text{Alt.}_B - R_A = \text{Azimuth}_A$$

In every case of subtraction, subtract the smaller from the larger number.

In Dreisonstok, the hour angles are given only up to 90 degrees. Ageton gives them up to 180 degrees. For values between 90 and 180 degrees, use the degrees given at the bottom of the column and take the odd minutes from the right-hand side. k is also taken from the bottom of the table.

The azimuth, called Z in these tables, is also taken from the bottom of the tables, except when k and L have the same sign, and k is greater than L. In this case the azimuth is taken from the top of the tables.

The sign of the azimuth is determined in the customary manner. It has the same sign as the latitude, and is east or west according to whether the hour angle is more or less than 180 degrees.

In these tables, when the hour angle is more than 180 degrees, subtract it from 360 degrees and use the remainder in the tables. For instance, if H. A. is 225 degrees, use $360° - 225° = 135°$ in solving the triangle. However, if you have done this you must remember that you have done so, and that the azimuth is E and not W, since H. A. is really 225 degrees.

Addenda

As in many other fields of endeavor, this progressive age has given us many changes in navigational theory and practice so that the present *American Nautical Almanac* represents another hurdle for the older generation to surmount, if we would "keep up with the times" and use our sextants intelligently *while they last*.

To those of our readers who are newly taking up the study of practical celestial navigation, we would point out that the problems used for illustration or exercise in this little book, where authentic astronomical data is required, originally involved use of the *1953 Almanac*. Where possible, therefore, these are retained, since use of the *1959 Almanac* would in no way affect or improve the purpose of such problem.

Hence, as the reader may observe, the choice of our "up-to-the-minute" *1959 Almanac* in some instances, although not indispensable, is deemed very desirable, in view of the late changes in presentation of data and consequent methods involved.

In this connection, you will find the present *Almanac* adopts the symbols *v* and *d*, instead of the term *code*, to denote hourly differences in G.H.A. and Declination, respectively, as used in the cases of the *Moon* and *Planets*.

Another small departure from the former *Almanacs* is that of the apparently minor place assigned the *Equation of Time*, with total omission of the algebraic sign for its application. It is true that a glance at the innovation "*Mer. Passage*" will show the true Sun *ahead* or *behind* the instant of Greenwich Mean Noon, or G.M.T. 12h., but it would be much clearer sailing to pick out a properly labeled *Equation* and thus avert that natural tendency to become the victim of a momentarily false image of the relative positions of *true* and *mean* Sun at Noon.

101

ALMANAC DATA CORRECTIONS

The G.H.A. of *Aries* (γ), *Venus, Mars, Jupiter, Saturn, Sun*, and *Moon* are given for each hour of G.M.T., the required corrections to be added for the odd minutes and seconds being tabulated under *Increments and Corrections* in the *Almanac's* yellow pages.

As a valuable mental check on your work of taking out required G.H.A. corrections, the odd minutes of G.M.T. divided by 4 will give the *exact* correction (in arc) to Sun's G.H.A., and a result so close to the truth in the cases of the respective *planets* and *Aries* as to be negligible. Thus, for G.M.T. Jan. 1, 15h. 35m. 20s., correction to be added to G.H.A. of *Sun, Aries,* or a *planet*, is simply (35m. 20s.) ÷ 4, expressed in arc, or 8° 50′; precisely true for the Sun and never in error more than 2½′ for *Aries* or a *planet*.

A little exercise in mentally converting minutes and seconds of *time* into degrees and minutes of *arc* will provide a worth-while timesaving device in thus by-passing the correction tables.

While we are considering "short cuts" in applying corrections, it should be realized that you have at your finger ends a "ready reckoner" in the *Traverse Tables*. Problems in ratio and proportion may be quickly solved by those proportional values which the tables represent, with almost any degree of accuracy desired.

Take, for example, the "correction for Longitude" included in the *Moon* problem on page 66: We see here that 360 bears the same ratio to 175 as 48m. to the required product. The Traverse Tables abreast of *Dist.* 360 show 174.5 as *Dep.* under *Course* 29°. So you find abreast of 48, under the same *Course*, 23.3, the number of minutes required.

Another Traverse Tables' use is in finding a distance sailed in a given number of minutes, as in the following: Speed 17 knots; what is distance run in 38 minutes? With 60 (minutes in 1 hour) in the *Dist.* column, nearest to 17 in *Dep.* column is 16.5 under 16° or 17.5 under 17°. Abreast of 38 (minutes run) you will find 10.5 under 16° and 11.1 under 17°. Obviously, the mean of these is the distance required, or 10.8 miles.

Or, to put it another way: With speed per hour as *Course*, find the distance run in the *Dep.* column abreast the minutes run in the *Dist.* column. With speeds up to 35 knots, the result will be within a half mile of the truth.

THE LINE OF POSITION

What has been stated anent the procedure of determining ship's position by celestial observations might here be supplemented by a few remarks worthy of the navigator's attention embracing some further applications of the *Sumner line* or *line of position*.

It should be remembered that any single observation by sextant altitude and corrected time, or a true bearing of a charted landmark, buoy, lightship, etc., will give you a *line of position*. Your ship is situated somewhere on such a line at the instant of observation, to repeat the remark on *page 12*.

This basic postulate may be put to practical use in several different ways apart from the determination of ship's position by two or more different heavenly bodies. Such uses of the line of position are noted in the following:

1. *Finding ship's position* by intersection of a radio bearing or that of a light, distant headland, mountain, or other known landmark, with the position line obtained from a single observation of a celestial body. This method frequently presents itself for use and the only condition required is that the lines intersect at a greater angle than about 30 degrees.

2. *Checking ship's course* by observation of a heavenly body whose bearing is approximately *abeam*. The resulting position line here lies closely parallel with ship's track and obviously conveys the information desired.

3. *Checking ship's speed* or distance made good. The position line resulting from the body observed bearing nearly *ahead* or nearly *astern* at once provides the necessary check.

4. *Clearing a danger* by the knowledge gained from a single line of position. This is a handy device when, uncertain of your ship's position, you are limited to a single line of position the projection of which indicates a course to steer clear of the danger. Often a sounding in such cases will serve as a timely warning or check on ship's advance along the "line".

5. From 2 and 3 it will be seen that, where the choice of stars is present, those bearing either nearly *ahead* or nearly *astern* will provide lines of position whose plotted directions are a check for accuracy in themselves. Lines laid at oblique angles with respect to ship's track have a happy knack of being laid 90° in error! (But *see page 11* for fundamentals on the *Line of Position*.)

Also to be considered is the means employed on a dark night when the sea horizon is indistinct. A star's altitude is taken by using a distant passing vessel's light as a substitute for the horizon. With a little practice at measuring the maximum altitude, or vertical angular distance between light and star, as both line up in azimuth, a most reliable line of position may be obtained by this means. Any small addition to the altitude, as obviously required by an apparent elevation of the light, must, of course, be estimated; but the method is capable of surprising accuracy.

In practice it often happens that the light in passing affords the advantage of a "fix" from a second observation taken as soon as the light's bearing will have changed sufficiently to give a well-defined "cut", or an angle of at least 30 degrees. Depending, of course, upon the availability of known stars, the elapsed time between the two observations rarely would exceed a half hour.

PLOTTING THE POSITION LINE

With reference to pages 40 and 44 concerning the projection of a *Line of Position* on the chart, you will eliminate any risk of error in determining the line's direction by simply considering the near-by parallel of latitude as a *meridian*. Draw the line as you would lay off a course or a bearing, at an angle equal to the azimuth (quadrantally named). Thus, in Diagram 16 on page 41, by laying off the position line as crossing the parallel of latitude 43° N. at an 86° angle, you will have automatically drawn the line at right angles to the star's azimuth.

GREAT CIRCLE OR AIR BEARING AND DISTANCE

What has been said concerning the point K in Section 11, pages 24-27, as the reader may have noted, naturally leads to the analogous procedure of determining the *Bearing* and *Distance* of one point from another on the earth's surface. If you indicate the point K, for example, as that of your destination, point A (see Diagram 12) as the place of departure, and the difference of longitude between them as the Hour Angle, you have the arguments for finding, from *H.O.214*, the *Great Circle Distance* AK and the *Initial Course* or local bearing of K.

Example: Find the *Initial Course* and the *Distance* in sailing or flying from Lat. 43° 00′ N., Long. 8° 50′ W. to Lat. 6° 50′ N., Long. 58° 10′ W.

Solution: At Lat. 43° (*Lat. and Dec. same name*) with 6° 50′ N. as *Dec.*, and 49° 20′ as *H.A.*, take from Table under *Dec.* 7° 00′ and abreast of 49°:

Alt.	34° 00.6′	*Az.* 115.4°
d corr.	−7.5′	or, *Initial Course* = N. 115° W.
t corr.	−13.4′	or, S. 65° W.
Alt.	= 33° 39.7′	or, 245°
	90°	
Z.D.	= 56° 20′	or *Dist.* = 56° 20′ × 60 = 3380 miles.

CHECKING CHRONOMETER ERROR

Section 14, page 28, deals with the necessary keeping of true *Greenwich Mean Time.* In the matter of being assured the daily rate of your Chronometer has not changed and in the event of time signals, or other means of obtaining the G.M.T., being unavailable, you have "another string to your bow" in *H.O. 214.*

The exact position of your vessel being known, an altitude of a body is observed and Chronometer time noted, or better, the *mean* of several altitudes and times. Then, with the estimated Chron. error, find the *G.M.T.* and thence the *G.H.A.* and *L.H.A.*

From *H.O. 214* take out the calculated *Alt.* corresponding to this *H.A.* and the *Az.* Then lay off the assumed *Line of Position* through known position of ship, also *Line of Position* obtained from the *intercept*, or difference between calculated and observed altitudes, as in usual observation procedure.

Then the intercepted distance as measured on nearest latitude parallel between the two position lines, or *D. Long.* (converted to time), represents the *correction* to be applied to your assumed or estimated Chronometer error.

Example: At about 3.00 p.m., April 8, 1959, off Cape Finisterre,
Lat. 42° 50′ N., Long. 8° 45′ W., the mean of 3 observed altitudes
of *Sun's* lower limb was 36° 30′, the mean of Chronometer readings
being 3h. 50m. 25s.   Estimated Chron. error 12m. 50s. fast.
Height of eye 25 feet.   Find correct Chronometer error.

Solution:

Chron. April 8, 15h. 50m. 25s.			*Sun's* Dec.	7° 04.4′ N.
Approx. error	−12m. 50s.		Corr.	+ .5′
Approx. G.M.T.	15h. 37m. 35s.		Dec.	7° 04.9′ N.

Sun's G.H.A. 15h.	= 44° 29.7′		*Sun's* L.L.	36° 30′
corr. for 37m. 35s.	+ 9° 23.8′		Dip	− 4.9′
Sun's G.H.A.	53° 53.5′		Corr.	+14.7′
Long. W.	8° 45.0′		*Alt.*	36° 39.8′
L.H.A.	= 45° 08.5′			

From *H.O. 214: Lat.* 43° N.; *H.A.* 45°:

Alt.	36°	36.8′
corr. for 5′*d*		+3.8′
” ” 8.5′ *t*		−5.4′
Calc. Alt.	= 36°	35.2′
Obs. Alt.	= 36°	39.8′
Toward		4.6′

Through Lat. 43° 00′ N., Long. 8° 45′ W. draw line of position
running N 29° W. and S 29° E. (331° and 151°), or at right angles
to *Az.* 119°.   Intercept 4.6′ toward the *Sun*, converted to *D. Long.*
in time, is then the correction to your estimated *Chron. error.*

Hence, this discrepancy between the calculated and the observed
altitudes, or *intercept*, in the case in question indicates a less
G.M.T. than was assumed, showing the Chronometer gains *more*
than allowed for.   We have, therefore, a *D. Long.* of 7.15′ = 28.6
secs. of time to be added to the estimated error, or, corrected
Chron. error is 12m. 50s. + 28.6s. = 13m. 19s. *fast.*

A working rule for applying the *D. Long.* intercept in time, or correction to your *estimated G.M.T.*, may be stated as follows:

Add the correction if *Az.* is E'ly and intercept is *toward;* or if *Az.* is W'ly and intercept is *away.*

Deduct correction if *Az.* is W'ly and intercept is *toward;* or if *Az.* is E'ly and intercept is *away.*

(The apparent behavior of the Chronometer will indicate whether such correction is to be added to, or deducted from, the *estimated Chron. error.*)

SEXTANT CORRECTIONS

On pages 22-23, the remarks on *Index Error*, also application of this correction to the "Sextant Altitude" as shown on pages 46 and 47, should not be taken too seriously by the beginner. The fact is that, once you have mastered the use of your instrument, you will allow no such "error" to bother you, but will adjust the sextant to read as it should. In this matter, you will find it profitable to follow *Bowditch's* chapter on the theory, practical use, and adjustment of the instrument.

PLANET'S MERIDIAN PASSAGE

In the present arrangement of the *Nautical Almanac*, it must be remembered that the times of transit of the *planets* are given for the middle day of the 3 on the page, or for every *third day*. Thus, for another day, time of transit must be found by interpolation.

Index

109

MEMORANDA

MEMORANDA

MEMORANDA

MEMORANDA

MEMORANDA